THE CELLULAR SLIME MOLDS

The Cellular Slime Molds

By JOHN TYLER BONNER

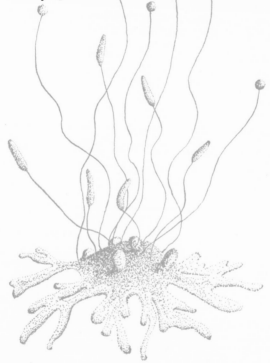

PRINCETON, NEW JERSEY

PRINCETON UNIVERSITY PRESS, 1959

John Tyler Bonner is Professor of Biology
at Princeton University.
He is author of three other books:
MORPHOGENESIS (Princeton, 1952),
CELLS AND SOCIETIES (Princeton, 1955), and
THE EVOLUTION OF DEVELOPMENT (Cambridge, 1958).

Preface

THE purpose of this monograph is twofold. First, an attempt has been made to give a comprehensive survey of all the different known aspects of the biology of the cellular slime molds. There has been a growing interest among experimental biologists working in widely different areas on these organisms, and therefore not only is the present status of the experimental knowledge stressed, but also life histories and relationships with other organisms, so that as complete a perspective as possible may be obtained. The field is yet young and the total amount of work done thus far is small, as the complete cellular slime mold bibliography in the back of the book will show. For this reason a thin volume is still possible, and it is hoped that in the years to come it will continue to serve as a useful summary of all the work done before 1959. But it must be admitted that this is not a mere summary of the field, for even though an effort has been made to include all the important facts, this is primarily an interpretation of these facts.

The cause of this may be found partly in human nature and partly in the second purpose of the book. The main reason that various workers have devoted so much of their energies to experimental studies of the cellular slime molds is that they are considered to be particularly useful organisms in the study of development. Therefore, inevitably, if one surveys and analyzes the literature, as has been done here, one hopes that by looking at all the known facts together, some new insights into the mechanism of development will appear. Writing this book has been of considerable value to me for just this reason, and I hope that it will serve as a useful stepping stone for the research of others in the future.

I should like to take this opportunity to thank Professor K. B. Raper, Dr. B. M. Shaffer and Professor C. H. Waddington for their kindness in reading the manuscript and providing many helpful suggestions and criticisms. Also I should like to acknowledge my indebtedness to the National Science Foundation and the Eugene Higgins Trust of Princeton University for financial assistance provided during the preparation of this book and during the current experimental work from our laboratory presented in this volume.

Finally, I am grateful to the following individuals for permission to use their illustrations: Drs. E. H. Mercer, K. B. Raper, B. M. Shaffer, and M. Sussman. I also wish to thank Miss Kathleen Dodge for her original drawings, Figs. 1, 2, 8, 9, 10, 11, 12.

Contents

CONTENTS

THE CELLULAR SLIME MOLDS

I. Aggregation Organisms

1. Slime molds

W HEN Brefeld made the first positive identification of a member of the Acrasiales in 1869, he mistakenly thought the cells fused to form a true plasmodium. This error was not corrected until 1880 when van Tieghem demonstrated that at all times the cells remained uninucleate; and to underscore the fact that there was no plasmodial syncytium in the Acrasiales, the aggregated cellular mass was called a "pseudoplasmodium." As the term implies, there was originally a strong belief in the close affinity of Myxomycetes and Acrasiales, but it has become increasingly clear, as our knowledge has advanced in recent years, that there is probably no phylogenetic relation between the two at all. They differ in so many particulars that to associate them, except by remote analogy, seems at the moment out of the question. The only feature that they have in common, and this is a source of infinite confusion, is the fact that they both are called "slime molds." There are very few textbooks of elementary biology that do not, because of this general term, completely confuse the two, and it is not uncommon to find an illustration of a member of the Acrasiales with a corresponding text description of a Myxomycete. To the discerning eye of a student of these lower groups this is an unpardonable error, equal to confusing a nematode and an annelid because they both are "worms."

To separate the two unrelated slime molds one may simply use the terms Myxomycetes or Myxogastrales for one and Acrasiales for the other. If common names are desired, the former have been called "plasmodial" or "true slime molds," and the Acrasiales have been called "simple slime molds" by K. B. Raper and "amoeboid slime molds" by myself. However, I am inclined to think that the most useful term is "cellular slime molds," the name suggested by B. M. Shaffer. To add to the confusion there are two other groups of organisms that are often associated with the slime molds already discussed, and all four of these may be conveniently classified in the following fashion:

> Mycetozoa
> Myxomycetales (or Myxogastrales)
> Plasmodiophorales
> Labyrinthulales
> Acrasiales

The logic of this grouping is that all four groups contain primitive colonial organisms that have both fungal and animal-like characters and all are to some extent slimy. Aside from these doubtful binding qualities they probably have little or no relation one to another. They are placed together because they represent four anomalous groups of unknown origin.

2. Myxomycetes

The Myxomycetes include some 400 species. Their fruiting bodies are macroscopic and easily recognizable on decaying wood or leaves. Most of the species bear their spores inside a sheath or peridium (Endosporeae), although individuals of the interesting genus *Ceratiomyxa* bear the spores singly on small papillae rising from the body of the mold (Exosporeae).

The life cycles of Myxomycetes were not completely understood until the work of Wilson and Cadman (1928) who were the first to unequivocally clarify the sexual nature of plasmodium formation. From their work and the work of others it is now possible to present a generalized life cycle that probably applies to all members of the group (Fig. 1).

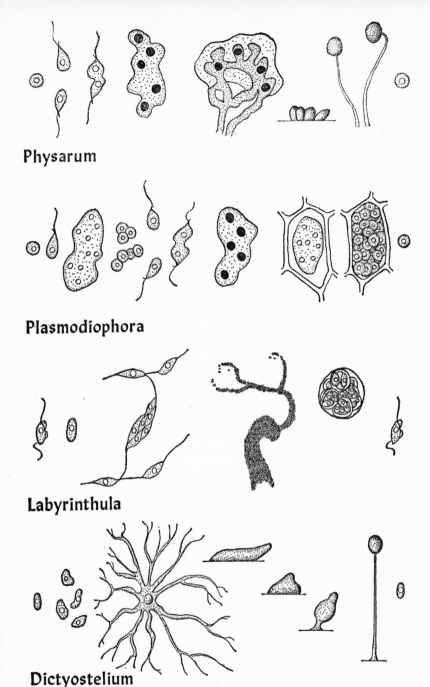

Physarum

Plasmodiophora

Labyrinthula

Dictyostelium

Fig. 1. The life cycles of representatives of the four groups of Mycetozoa. (From top to bottom) Myxomycetales, Plasmodiophorales, Labyrinthulales, and Acrasiales. In the first two, where sexuality is well established, diploid nuclei are indicated by solid black dots while haploid nuclei are white. Also the first two are the only ones showing a plasmodial stage. In each the cycle begins (left) and ends (right) with a unicellular spore.

The delicately sculptured spore germinates to liberate a haploid swarmer. In some cases the spore liberates four such swarmers and in others a single swarmer may divide into four daughter swarmers. Either immediately after germination or after cell divisions, if they occur, the cells sprout two flagella, one very much longer than the other. These flagella may subsequently be reabsorbed with the return of the amoeboid condition. The important point is that these cells, either at the flagellated or amoeboid stage, may serve as gametes and fuse in pairs. The resulting diploid cell is the fertilized "egg" that gives rise to the plasmodium, and now there follows a series of nuclear divisions without corresponding cell cleavages, and the protoplasmic mass begins a great period of expansion.

During this rapid growth the young plasmodium acts like a large amoeba, engulfing bacteria and other organic particles. In fact, it was the cannibalistic engulfing of other swarmers that was misinterpreted for many years as the mechanism of plasmodium formation; it was thought that many swarmers contributed their nuclei as genetic material to the one plasmodium. But now that the sexual mechanism is properly understood, we know that the contribution of the foreign nuclei is not genetic but simply a source of food.

Under the proper environment of nutriment, temperature, and moisture, the size of the plasmodium may increase to a few inches or more in diameter, and it is a common observation to see on a decayed stump in a wet forest a glistening viscous mass of slime, frequently a brilliant yellow. If adverse conditions should suddenly arise, the plasmodium can contract into a thickened, hardened mass. This so-called sclerotium may be stored in a dry condition for some time, but it will soften and release a viable plasmodium after being replaced in a favorable environment.

Sporangium formation is a more organized affair. The protoplasm tends to concentrate in a limited region and there becomes cut up into a series of compartments; each of these rises into a small bleb which will develop into a sporangium. This concentration of the protoplasm of the diffuse, spread out, vegetative, feeding plasmodium is the only part of Myxomycete development that could in any way be construed as an aggregation. And it is so in only a limited sense; that of the coming together of its constituent parts. But all the parts are the product of one zygote nucleus and there is no possibility here of the aggregation of numerous, genetically different nuclei. The importance of this distinction will become more evident when the life cycles of other slime molds are discussed.

In stalked forms the blebs rise into the air. The protoplasm flows upward, depositing centrally a stalk of non-living material. After the bulk of the protoplasm has reached its apical position, an outside wall or peridium is secreted. A series of furrows form, so that ultimately each nucleus is isolated in a block of protoplasm. Either before or during this process the nuclei undergo meiosis, so that the final isolated nuclei are haploid; each of these then secretes a cellulose wall to become a resistant spore. In some species a material is secreted in the larger cracks resulting from progressive cleavage which hardens to form a thread-like capillitium. Depending on the species, this capillitium may be delicately sculptured as well as hygroscopic, thereby helping the process of spore dispersal.

The variety of shapes of the fruiting bodies is great, and it is used as the basis of their classification. Some species have no stalk but are merely rounded or flattened masses projecting from the substratum. The majority are stalked, but the stalk may be single or branched. The great variation comes in the details of the structure of the stalk and the capillitium, the shape of the peridium, and the sculpturing of the spores.

3. Plasmodiophorales

The Plasmodiophorales are a group of organisms which have been principally of interest to the plant pathologist, for all the known species, of which there are some thirty, are plant parasites. They are most noticeably destructive among cabbages, and the clubroot disease of cabbage was a great scourge some years back; now that effective methods of control are known, it is no longer of importance.

As will be seen from an examination of Karling's (1942) volume on Plasmodiophorales, there is some variation in the cycle of different members of the group and even some variation in the interpretation of these cycles by different workers. Here I shall confine the discussion to Cook and Schwartz's (1930) description of *Plasmodiophora brassica*, which is the specific agent of the clubroot disease of cabbage (Fig. 1).

The spore of the mold germinates to produce a biflagellate swarmer, again with one flagellum shorter than the other. As a matter of fact, the double nature of the flagella was first discovered in the Plasmodiophorales in 1934 by Ledingham, and only subsequently was the small second flagellum observed in the Myxomycetes. This swarmer penetrates the root of a cabbage seedling and becomes, inside a cell of the plant, a myxamoeba by reabsorbing its flagella. The swarmer (and also the myxamoeba) is haploid; therefore the plasmodium which results from mitotic divisions of the original nucleus of the myxamoeba is haploid and has no counterpart in the life cycle of Myxomycetes. The haploid plasmodium is minute, not exceeding thirty nuclei, and when it stops growing it cleaves, cutting off a number of haploid, uninucleate cells. Each of these is in fact a gametangium; by division each produces four or eight flagellated gametes. The gametes fuse to produce a diploid myxamoeba, and this myxamoeba, again by mitotic divisions, will produce a plasmodium which in this case will be diploid. Either at the uninucleate stage or after a few nuclear divisions the parasite becomes highly invasive and bores its way from one cell to another, in this way entering the cambium of the cabbage, passing to various parts of the root, and finally wandering out into the cortex. The plasmodium now becomes large and produces a corresponding effect in the cabbage root which thickens into the club-like swellings. Eventually the plasmodium undergoes meiosis and progressive cleavage to form numerous haploid spores.

Concerning the relationship of the Myxomycetes and the Plasmodiophorales, it should be noted that they are both of flagellate origin, but this is also true of the majority of colonial animals and plants. It was the old traditional view that the two groups were closely associated, one being parasitic and the other, free-living. However, with increased knowledge it became obvious that they differ in so many ways, such as the cytological details and the haploid plasmodium of the Plasmodiophorales, that the modern trend has been to consider the Myxomycetes a discrete group, with the Plasmodiophorales related to the lower filamentous fungi or Phycomycetes. This is based largely on similarities between Plasmodiophorales and Chytrids, the details of which would be superfluous in this discussion. There is a good possibility that each of these three groups, the Myxomycetes, the Plasmodiophorales, and the Chytrids, arose independently from flagellate ancestry. Perhaps all we can assert with confidence is that the origin and relationship of these groups is doubtful.

4. Labyrinthulales

This group is composed of one genus, *Labyrinthula*, and a mere handful of species. They also are parasites and are of considerable ecological importance, for as Renn (1935) showed, they were responsible for the wasting disease of eel grass which did so much to change the whole aspect of our coasts some twenty years ago.

These marine parasites infect not only eel grass but many algae as well. The vegetative cell is spindle-shaped and produces a projection of material from each end, much as a developing nerve cell of an animal produces its axone. These projections of *Labyrinthula* form a network, and the uninucleate cells proceed to glide up and down it, travelling only on the tracks they have previously laid down. This pattern of growth has been given the unfortunate name of "net plasmodium." It does indeed form a net, but since the cells are at all times uninucleate, it is in no way a plasmodium. The spindle cells occasionally aggregate into a dense mass and each cell becomes encapsulated into a spore, but again without any syncytium. Therefore, these now represent true aggregation organisms, in a sense, although this aggregation is of such a crude and primitive nature that it fails to provide the opportunities for experimental analysis found in the Acrasiales.

Until recently there had been no indication of any flagellated cells, nor any evidence of sexuality. Independently, Hollande and Enjumet (1955), and Watson (1955) discovered the presence of biflagellate swarmers, but there still has been no demonstration of sexuality in the life cycle of these organisms (Fig. 1).

The phylogeny of *Labyrinthula* represents a special problem, and Smith (1955) rejects it from his general slime mold category, Myxomycophyta, on the basis that it shows similarities to the golden alga *Chlorarachnion*. The possibility that Smith is correct in the conjecture that *Labyrinthula* is an alga which has lost its photosynthetic pigments upon becoming parasitic, is certainly reasonable and not disputed. I would, however, not exclude it from the group of slime molds on this basis, but quite to the contrary, would consider that because of its possibly unique origin, it has passed the test of not being related to the other slime molds and therefore can be a member of this heterogeneous group of Mycetozoa.

5. Acrasiales

My intention in this section is to give only a brief picture of the Acrasiales for purposes of comparison with the other slime molds. At the moment a dozen species of the Acrasiales are known, all of which are free-living in the soil. The germinating spores liberate a single uninucleate amoeba; there are no flagellated cells. The amoebae feed on bacteria by phagocytosis and repeatedly divide by mitosis, each daughter cell remaining uninucleate and free and independent of the other cells. When a large number of such separate amoebae have accumulated, they will stream together to central collection points to form a cell mass or pseudoplasmodium. This concentration of cells involves no fusion of protoplasts, but the uninucleate character of the cells is maintained following aggregation and during all the other phases of the life cycle (Fig. 1).

One important point here is that there is a natural separation between feeding stages and the morphogenetic stages. Feeding will cease some time before aggregation, usually as the result of the depletion of the food supply, and from that moment on the energy for the morphogenetic stages comes entirely from the reserves stored up in the vegetative stage. In the Myxomycetes the feeding also comes first and is followed by fruiting. This separation cannot readily be demonstrated in the Plasmodiophorales because of their parasitic habit, and thus far there is no evidence for it in the Labyrinthulales.

The fate of the cell mass following aggregation depends to a great extent upon the species. In some there is a period of migration of the cell mass for variable intervals of time. Generally there are signs of differentiation of two cell types. The anterior cells begin to form a stalk at the apex. The stalk consists of large vacuolate cells enclosed in a delicate tapering cylinder of cellulose. It is formed by the cells at the periphery of the apex moving up to the top and becoming trapped in the stalk proper. Once there, the amoebae begin to swell in a gradual conversion to the large pith-like stalk cells. As this occurs, the cellulose of the stalk is continuously deposited around them.

The posterior cells are to become the sorus. Again there is variation among species, but usually the whole posterior portion is lifted as one mass into the air, so that it forms an apical glob of cells when the stalk formation is completed. Each amoeba in this mass of cells becomes encapsulated in a hard cellulose spore case, ready for germination and the next generation.

These cellular slime molds represent an excellent example of aggregation organisms, for during the aggregation process there is a coming together of cells, and these cells may or may not be of precisely the same genetic constitution. It is in every sense a gathering, and not merely a concentration of protoplasm in one spot, the latter being more the situation in the Myxomycetes. Furthermore, as a result of the aggregation one organism is made out of many; in the span of a few hours, without the help of growth, the separate cells come together to form a unified, coordinated, multicellular individual.

Concerning the phylogeny of the Acrasiales, the old tradition that they bear some relation to the Myxomycetes should undoubtedly be abandoned. The principal differences between the two are the total absence of a flagellated stage and the absence of the syncitial plasmodium in the Acrasiales.

Another point of divergence is the clear-cut sexuality in the Myxomycetes, where the zygote nucleus gives rise to the whole plasmodium. There is still insufficient evidence to support the notion of sexuality in the Acrasiales, despite the work of Skupienski (1920) and Wilson (1952, et seq.), although the possibility that future work may show the cellular slime molds to be sexual cannot be neglected. However, if there is to be an analogy to the sexuality of Myxomycetes, syngamy should begin after spore germination, and the mass of vegetative amoebae which enter ultimately into aggregation should be diploid. The fact that there are seven chromosomes during vegetative division (a fact which I have been able to observe in a few cases), clearly indicates that the vegetative amoebae are haploid. It is my view that this difference is a major reason for considering the two groups to be totally independent in their origin.

What then is the origin of the Acrasiales? To the Myxomycetes we ascribed a flagellate ancestry; the same was true of the Plasmodiophorales, with the possibility that the specific flagellate was allied to the Chytrid fungi; the Labyrinthulales are also flagellated, and Smith's suggestion of their relation to the golden algae is reasonable. The most likely origin of the Acrasiales is from the free-living amoebae of the soil. There are many amoebae which have no flagellated stage and no established sexuality; their life cycle consists of a free-wandering stage followed by a period of encystment. This idea is by no means new, and a number of the earlier workers from de Bary (1887) on have made this suggestion; it still has much to recommend it. It should be remembered that it is presumed that the free-living amoebae themselves stem from the flagellates, for there is a close relation between pseudopod and flagellum. This means then that all four groups of Mycetozoa have, according to our argument, separate and independent origins from the flagellates. Obviously this feature is not unique with them, for different groups of algae, fungi, and other plants, as well as sponges and other animals all have had similar independent origins.

6. Other aggregative organisms

It is a curious paradox that the organisms that most closely resemble the Acrasiales in their life history, the Myxobacteria, are completely unrelated. Their similarity was recognized by Thaxter (1892) who discovered the group.

In the larger, more conspicuous members of the Myxobacteria such as *Chondromyces*, the resistant bodies are cysts which enclose many rod-shaped bacterial cells. If sown in a suitable environment, they split open and produce a stream of rods that soon begin their period of vegetative growth. During this phase there is a marked tendency for the cells to stick together and follow one another's tracks as they glide smoothly along. Therefore, in a sense, they aggregate continually, and if two groups are in close proximity they will merge. There is in this merger some evidence of mutual attraction which could conceivably be chemotaxis (see Bonner, 1952).

Fruiting begins by a clump of cells becoming rounded, drawing itself up from the surface of the agar, and rising into the air. The bacterial rods produce much slime which is left behind as the rods themselves seek an uppermost position, so that a stalk made up largely of this exudate forms in the rear. As the mass of rods advances it may bifurcate, ultimately producing a number of globular masses at the end of the branched, exuded stalk. Each one of the masses now becomes carved out by indentation into a cluster of cysts, and these cysts remain viable for long periods of time in unfavorable growth conditions.

If we search elsewhere for examples of aggregation organisms, we will find one case that is especially well known and well understood, namely the development of Ascomycetes. These fungi have the ability to produce hyphal fusions, and in this way there can be aggregations of nuclei of various genetic constitutions. The nuclei do not fuse but remain in the haploid condition, intermingling in the cytoplasm, a condition known as heterocaryosis. This fusion of genetic strains may not involve an immediate large concentration of protoplasm as was the case in the Acrasiales, but in a modified way this does occur. In the first place, it has been shown that the nuclei can move large distances fairly rapidly in the mycelial network; secondly, when spore formation occurs, either sexual or asexual, there is an aggregation or flow of protoplasm within the vegetative mycelium to the fruiting structure.

Other examples are harder to find. In a sense the development of the green alga *Enteromorpha minima* shows some aggregative properties. In related species of *Enteromorpha* the young plant develops from a single swarm cell that attaches to the ocean floor. In *E. minima* Bliding (1938) showed that a whole mass of swarmers develop in an area, each producing young shoots which in turn fuse to form one individual. It is a case in which there is no apparent inward migration of material or mutual attraction (at least none has been demonstrated among the swarmers), but the individual does have numerous parents and a polyglot genetic constitution.

7. The significance of aggregation in biology

The significance of aggregation has been discussed previously in some detail (Bonner, 1958), and here I would like to emphasize briefly three points.

The first is that the aggregation process may serve as a partial substitute for sexuality. As Haldane (1955) has pointed out in the case of Ascomycetes, there is a gathering of diverse nuclei in the heterocaryon and then by the production of many haploid spores these nuclei are segregated so they may again combine in other ways upon subsequent germination and fusions. Such a system has the advantage over sexuality that there can be more than two parents, but it lacks the advantage of chromosomal recombination that can result from the formation of diploid nuclei and the subsequent meiosis.

In the Acrasiales it is not merely a matter of nuclei, but of whole cells coming together in the aggregation. Yet the same point applies, since the nuclei of many parents are gathered in one sorus, which can then be redistributed in the uninucleate spores to form new combinations. The fact that the cellular slime molds have this substitution for sex, this recombination on a cellular level, does not mean that a truly sexual system might not exist as well; in fact, the Ascomycetes have both systems. On the other hand, it is conceivable that such a system of handling and recombining variants is adequate for the Acrasiales, as it is for many of the imperfect fungi. It should be added that all these arguments apply to the Myxobacteria as well.

The second point concerning the significance of aggregation is the possibility that for some forms this is the channel by which a truly multicellular condition has been achieved. If one postulates that separate cells living in close proximity developed mutual deficiencies so that they became dependent upon each other, then it would follow that there would be a selective pressure in favor of an aggregative mechanism. There is, therefore, the possibility that cells with genetically determined nutritive deficiencies benefit from aggregation to some extent, in the way that cells benefit by sexual fusion. Both aggregation as well as sexuality provide genetic advantages for association. This being the case, we have a rational understanding of a possible evolutionary reason for the existence of aggregation and the production of multicellular individuals by aggregation. Obviously there are other ways in which multicellular organisms came into being; aggregation is merely one of the possibilities.

The third and last point is the importance of aggregation as a tool in the study of the mechanisms of development. There are many aspects of development which have remained refractory to interpretation, and of these perhaps the most important is the mechanism of regulation: the fact that a group of cells with equal potencies may be cut, fused, or redistributed, yet the cell mass as a whole will give rise to a perfect individual. One of the difficulties in attacking this problem has been that in conventional embryos which arise from a fertilized egg there is a mixture of growth and a segregation of potencies along with periods of partial regulation.

If cells cleave, there may be a separation of cell components, and many workers in recent years have emphasized that with cleavage one may have either nuclear or cytoplasmic differences in the cell progeny. There has been, for instance, a rash of statements on the bearing of cytoplasmic inheritance on differentiation. I do not deny the possibility of a segregation of materials and determinants during cleavage, nor the possibility that this might lead to differentiation. Nevertheless, this cannot be the whole picture.

This is so because there are cases of differentiation in which all the cells can be demonstrated to be equipotent; there is no cell division to pass determinants into one cell line and not the other. This mass of non-dividing, equipotential cells will proceed to differentiate, and the fate of a cell, following the dictum of Driesch, will be a function of its position. This cannot even be approached in terms of the conventional view of cell inheritance, and any easy analogy between the genetics of microorganisms and the development of such a purely regulative system is bound to be inadequate.

Aggregative organisms, and in particular the cellular slime molds afford almost perfect examples of such regulatory behavior. They are made up of a group of equipotential cells which do not arise in specific sites in an embryo, but grow separately and then come together by piling on top of one another. This suggests that the possibilities of cell arrangement during aggregation are numerous, yet each combination produces a normal individual. But, as will be shown, there is the possibility of cell rearrangement within the mass, and furthermore, despite the fact that the cells are equipotent, there is ample room for variation among them, and there is a good possibility that cell variation is involved in subtle ways in the process of differentiation. In fact, it will be important to examine the problem of variation on all levels and from all aspects in the Acrasiales in order to obtain a better understanding of both the mechanism of inheritance and the mechanism of development in these organisms.

Before this is possible, it will be necessary first to examine the nature of the different members of the Acrasiales in detail, as well as to discuss what is known of the mechanics of their development.

II. The Cellular Slime Molds

1. A brief survey of the Acrasiales

THE first comprehensive view of the cellular slime molds is the monograph of the Acrasieae by Olive, published in 1902. Since then the taxonomic approach to these organisms has been carried out almost solely by Raper. Unfortunately, to date he has published his results and his views on this subject only as small parts of papers dealing primarily with other matters (1940a, 1951, 1956a), but we may hope that this ultimately will lead to a detailed taxonomic study of the Acrasieae.

Below I have given a list of the families, genera, and species of the cellular slime molds. It is based primarily on Raper's modifications of Olive. After this brief summary each group will be described in more detail (Fig. 2).

Sappiniaceae
    Sappinia Dangeard, 1896.   Common.
Guttulinaceae
    Guttulinopsis Olive, 1901. Olive describes three species in this genus, but it has not been examined in detail since.
    Guttulina Cienkowsky, 1873.   There are four species described in this genus by Cienkowsky, Fayod (1883), and van Tieghem (1880), but again it has not been examined in detail.

Dictyosteliaceae
    Dictyostelium
        Dictyostelium discoideum Raper, 1935. Isolated relatively infrequently.

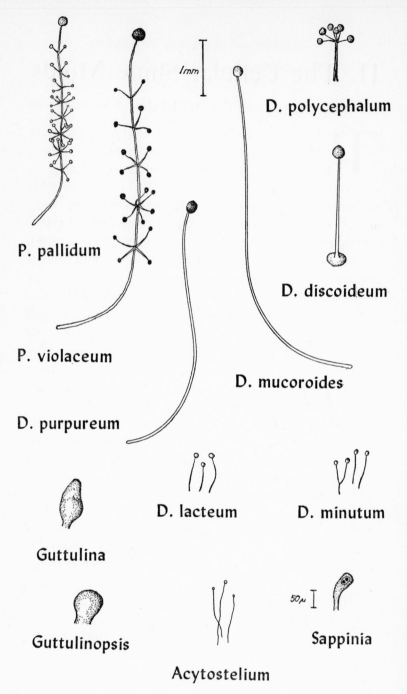

P. pallidum

P. violaceum

D. purpureum

Guttulina

Guttulinopsis

1mm

D. polycephalum

D. discoideum

D. mucoroides

D. lacteum

D. minutum

Acytostelium

50μ

Sappinia

Fig. 2. The mature fruiting bodies of the different species of Acrasiales known today.

Dictyostelium mucoroides Brefeld, 1869. This is perhaps best described as a "complex," for there is great variation in this group. (Raper, 1951). Probably a number of the *Dictyostelium* species listed by Olive fall within this complex, as may also *D. giganteum* of Singh (1947a). Very common.

Dictyostelium purpureum Olive, 1901. Common.

Dictyostelium minutum Raper, 1941a. There is the possibility suggested by Raper (1941a) that this species is a diminutive *D. mucoroides* and therefore should appropriately be part of the mucoroides "complex." Relatively infrequent.

Dictyostelium lacteum van Tieghem, 1880. Unknown until it was rediscovered by Raper (1951). Rare.

Dictyostelium polycephalum Raper, 1956b. Rare.

Polysphondylium

Polysphondylium violaceum Brefeld, 1884. Very common.

Polysphondylium pallidum Olive, 1901. Olive also lists another white-spored species of *Polysphondylium*, but as Raper (1951) points out, this quite likely merely represents variation in the *pallidum* group. Common.

Acytostelium

Acytostelium leptosomum Raper, 1956a. Rare

There are two genera that are known only from their original descriptions and unfortunately have not been rediscovered.

Acrasis van Tieghem, 1880.
Coenonia van Tieghem, 1884.

2. Sappiniaceae

There has been grave doubt as to whether *Sappinia* should be included among the Acrasiales or more appropriately retained among the free-living soil amoebae. The main criterion for its inclusion is that there are occasional aggregations of cells in a sorus at the ends of sticks or bits of debris in the culture, but this appears not to be an organized aggregation process but a fortuitous accident dependent upon the contours of the objects covering the substratum. In this it resembles more the clumping of encysted amoebae found in the soil amoeba *Hartmanella astronyxis* described by Ray and Hayes (1954).

Another similarity to Acrasiales is the stalked cyst. The fact that an amoeba can secrete stalk material so that during its encystment it will be lifted off the ground is indeed similar to what is found in some of the other Acrasiales, especially the new genus of Raper, *Acytostelium*, where a group of amoebae secrete a stalk that is non-cellular.

The point of greatest difference is the fact that *Sappinia* is binucleate. This, however, is of interest because of the possibility that here may be a case of a true heterocaryon (or dicaryon) in an amoeba. It has been studied in *Sappinia diploidea* by Hartmann and Nägler (1908), and Nägler (1909), and according to Wenrich (1954) it represents the only acceptable case of demonstrated true sexuality in free-living amoebae, although even here there remain some points that need further clarification. The haploid nuclei of *Sappinia* lie side by side and divide simultaneously at each binary fission. During the sexual process two amoebae come together to form a common cyst. The two nuclei of each amoeba then fuse (similar to the delayed caryogamy of Basidiomycetes), and then finally the protoplasts fuse. Both diploid nuclei now undergo two reduction divisions, during each of which one of the daughter nuclei degenerates. The final two remaining haploid nuclei are the normal complement of the vegetative, dicaryon individual which then emerges from the cyst.

Despite being interesting in its own right, there is nothing in this cycle that has a counterpart in other members of the Acrasiales. Even the cytological observations of Wilson (1952, 1953; Wilson and Ross, 1957) on *Dictyostelium discoideum* could in no way be homologized with this work on *Sappinia*. It is true that occasionally in stained preparations of higher cellular slime molds it is possible to see binucleate cells, but these are very infrequent and must be presumed to have occurred accidentally and to play no role in the normal life history. Furthermore, in such cases the two nuclei do not lie side by side as in *Sappinia*, but are separate in the common protoplasm. Yet in spite of all these differences in detail, it is still reasonable to assume that the cellular slime molds arose from some *Sappinia*-like ancestor, although the connection may be so remote that *Sappinia* more properly should remain among the protozoa.

3. Guttulinaceae

The genera *Guttulina* and *Guttulinopsis* can without hesitation be included among the Acrasiales. Both genera are characterized by somewhat amorphous, irregular fruiting bodies that may either be stalked or sessile; they have none of the delicacy of the members of Dictyosteliaceae. In some cases the stalk appears to be a distinct structure with cells that are firmly cemented together, while often all the cells of the fruiting body will disintegrate when touched; presumably each cell is viable and can start a new generation.

The difference between *Guttulina* and *Guttulinopsis* is that in the former there are true spores and in the latter there are pseudospores—cells which have become hardened and somewhat crinkled but do not form a smooth spore case. It was an early conjecture that the pseudospore was a primitive spore and that *Guttulinopsis* was an ancestral member of the Acrasiales. This position has its difficulties; for instance, many of the soil amoebae have beautifully organized and sculptured cysts. In fact, the opposite view that *Guttulina* and *Guttulinopsis* illustrate varying degrees of degeneration of members of the Dictyosteliaceae has perhaps more to recommend it.

Following this thought, Singh (1947a) made the suggestion that *Guttulina* and its relatives are representative of the Dictyosteliaceae growing in unfavorable circumstances. Pinoy (1950) found a form that corresponded closely with Cienkowski's (1873) description of *Guttulina rosea*. By changing the bacterial associate as well as the medium, he was able to obtain fruiting bodies of *Dictyostelium mucoroides*. Unfortunately this is described only in a short note published posthumously, and he says that although the experiments were done in 1930, the cultures died during the summer and he was unable to pursue the matter. One wonders, for instance, if his original innoculum might have consisted of two species.

Cohen (1953a) has performed a careful and extensive analysis of the same phenomenon and shown that specifically free ammonia is responsible for producing *Guttulina*-like fruiting bodies in different species of *Dictyostelium* and *Polysphondylium*, and from this work he implies that the genera *Guttulina* and *Guttulinopsis* ought to be eliminated.

This idea is firmly contested by Raper (1956a), who has

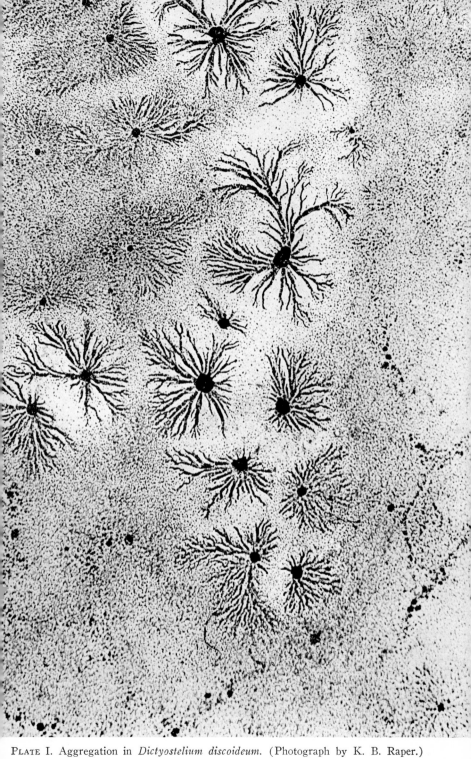

PLATE I. Aggregation in *Dictyostelium discoideum*. (Photograph by K. B. Raper.)

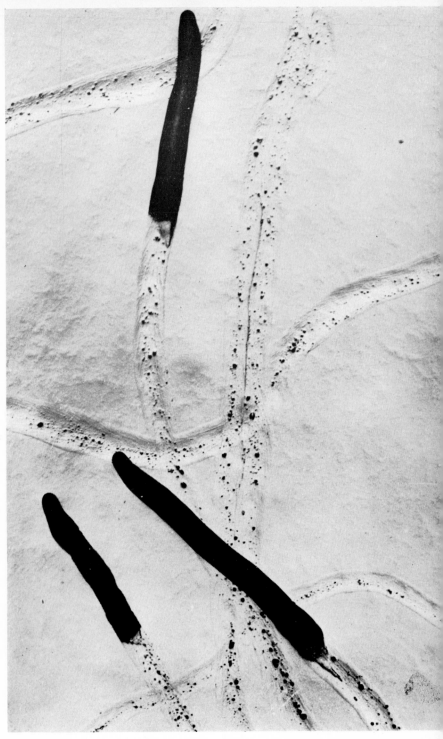

PLATE II. Migrating pseudoplasmodia of *Dictyostelium discoideum* showing the slime tracks which are left behind on the agar. (Photograph by K. B. Raper.)

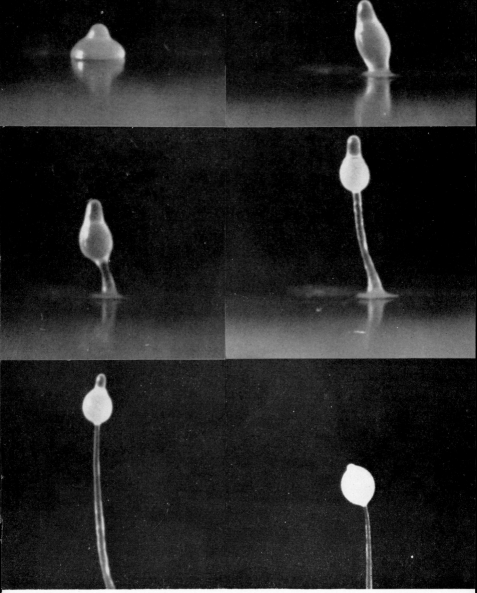

PLATE III. Culmination of *Dictyostelium discoideum*. Each photograph represents a time interval of approximately one and one half hours.

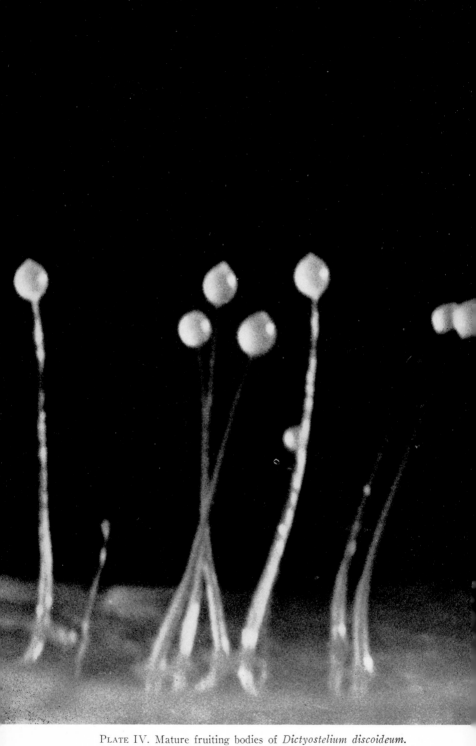

PLATE IV. Mature fruiting bodies of *Dictyostelium discoideum.*

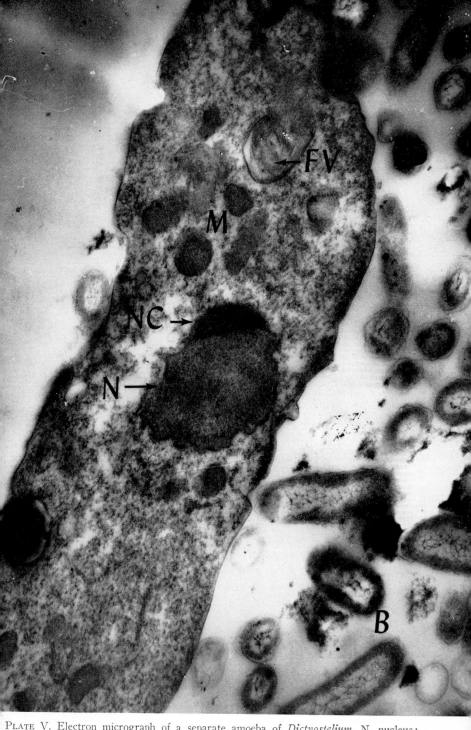

PLATE V. Electron micrograph of a separate amoeba of *Dictyostelium*. N, nucleus; NC, polar cap of nucleus; M, mitochondria; FV, food vacuole; B, bacteria. 25,000x. (Photograph by E. H. Mercer and B. M. Shaffer.)

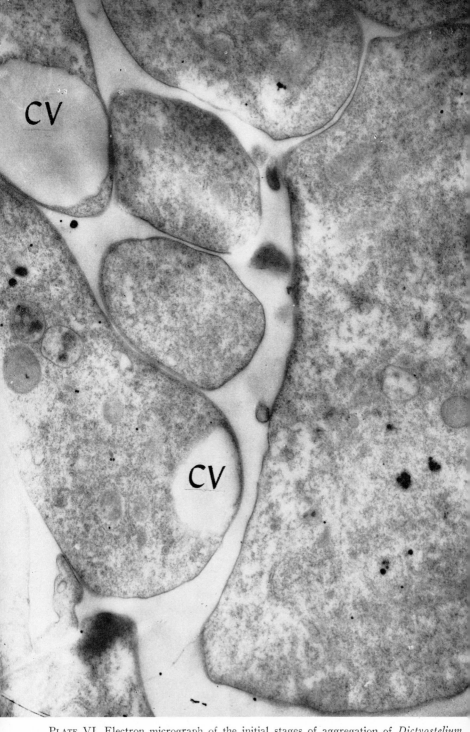

PLATE VI. Electron micrograph of the initial stages of aggregation of *Dictyostelium* showing loose contact between cells. CV, contractile vacuole. 25,000x. (Photograph by E. H. Mercer and B. M. Shaffer.)

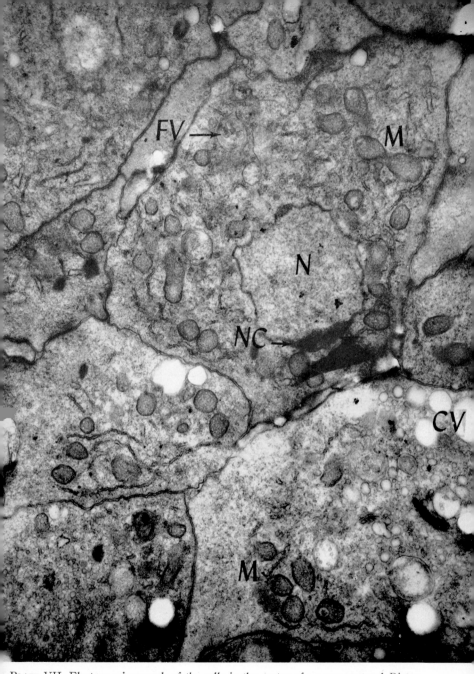

PLATE VII. Electron micrograph of the cells in the center of an aggregate of *Dictyostelium*, showing intimate contact between cells. Note that the adjacent plasma membranes do not meet but are separated by a thin gap resembling tissues of more organized multicellular organisms. N, nucleus; NC, polar cap of nucleus; M, mitochrondria; FV, food vacuole; CV, contractile vacuole. 25,000x. (Photograph by E. H. Mercer and B. M. Shaffer.)

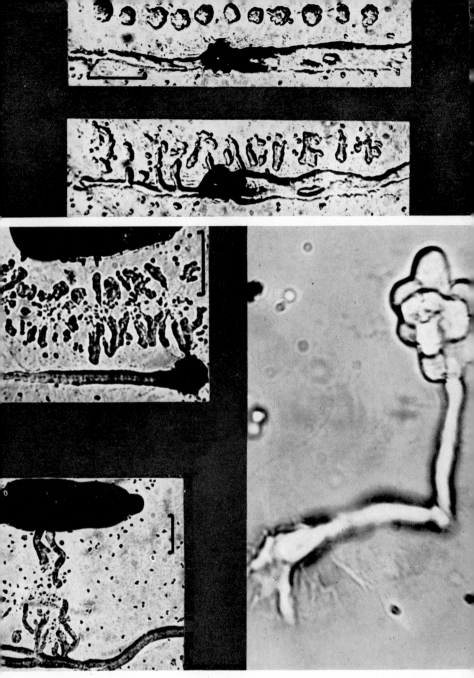

PLATE VIII. *Upper pair of photographs*: Groups of responsive amoebae were placed near an aggregation pattern of *Dictyostelium mucoroides* and they showed equal tendencies to enter both the center and the streams. *Left hand pair of photographs*: Responsive amoebae placed between fruiting bodies and aggregation streams of *Dictyostelium mucoroides* showed an equal tendency to enter both structures. These are the experiments of B. M. Shaffer to show that there is the same amount of acrasin emitted from streams, centers and pseudoplasmodia. The scale represents 200 μ. (Photographs by B. M. Shaffer.) *Lower right*: Photograph of a small fruiting body of Sussman's mutant "fruity," possessing two stalk cells and nine spores. (Photograph by M. Sussman.)

certain strains of stalkless and pseudo-stalked forms that retain their *Guttulina*-like character under all cultural conditions. Further light is shed on the matter by the fact that Sussman and Sussman (1953), Sussman (1954a) have produced mutants of members of the Dictyosteliaceae, a few of which have some *Guttulina* characteristics. Undoubtedly there are such forms which permanently possess this character, as Raper suggests, but their taxonomic treatment (especially as we are dealing here with a presumed asexual organism) is a matter which must be approached with care.

4. *Dictyostelium discoideum*

More is known by far of the morphological details of this species than any other (Fig. 3; Plates I, II, III, IV). This is largely because ever since its discovery by Raper in 1935, its potentialities as an experimental organism have been appreciated and it has been intensively studied.

A host of different methods have been used in the descriptive work. The groundwork was laid down by Raper (1935. 1940a, 1940b, 1941; Raper and Fennell, 1952), who by culturing the organism on different media and under different environmental conditions, by making stained whole mounts, and by cutting and grafting experiments, was able to obtain a comprehensive picture of the life cycle. Some details were added by Raper's motion picture of the migration phase.

Following the lead of Arndt (1937) with his motion picture of *D. mucoroides* (taken in 1929), I made a time lapse film of the whole cycle of *D. discoideum* in 1941 (and have added to it subsequently). This proved most helpful in understanding many of the details of development.

The use of histological sections also has been rewarding (Bonner, 1944), for in this way it is possible to follow with some accuracy the internal cellular details. At first, rather

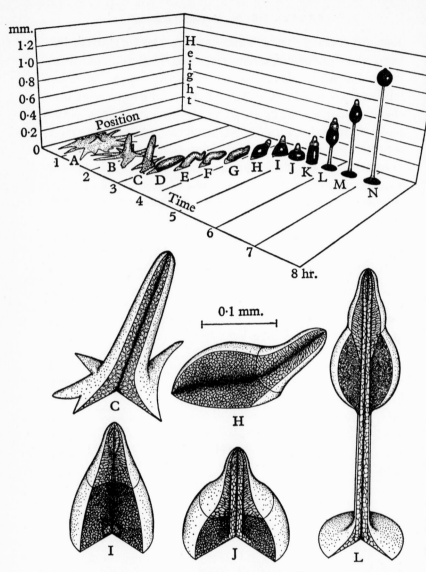

Fig. 3. Development in *Dictyostelium discoideum*. The complete morphogenesis is represented in a three-dimensional graph. A-C, aggregation; D-H, migration; I-N, culmination. The presence of prespore cells is indicated by heavy stippling, H-K; and the presence of spores by solid black, L-N. *Below*: semi-diagrammatic drawings showing the cell structure at different stages. The letters indicate the corresponding stages given above.

standard methods using haemotoxylin were employed, but later, more modern histochemical methods were found most helpful (Bonner, Chiquoine, and Kolderie, 1955). This also has been pursued by Krivanek (1956) along with some biochemical analyses. More extensive biochemical analyses of the mold at different stages of development (morphology on a strictly chemical level) have been performed by Gregg, Hackney, and Krivanek (1954), and Gregg and Bronsweig (1956).

There also has been some work on the cytological level, especially on the nuclear phenomena (Wilson, 1952, 1953; Wilson and Ross, 1957; Bonner and Frascella, 1952; Labudde, 1956), and finally, there is a useful study of *D. discoideum* with electron micrographs of ultrathin sections and other preparations by Mühlethaler (1956) and another independent study by Gezelius and Rånby (1957).

The following description of each stage of the life cycle of *D. discoideum* is based primarily on the references given above. I will not attempt on all points to give the details of which particular author made the original observation; my object is to describe the slime mold rather than write a history. Also it should be mentioned that occasional observations were made originally on some other species and the information transferred to *D. discoideum*. This is an obvious consequence of the fact that *D. discoideum* has been discovered relatively recently.

5. Spores and spore germination in *D. discoideum*

The spores of *D. discoideum* are elliptical in shape. Their size varies considerably, being approximately 6 to 9 μ long and 2.5 to 3.5 μ in diameter. The nuclear size, which may be easily measured in Feulgen preparations, shows a range of diameters from 0.8 to 2.5 μ. Nuclear stains reveal little in the way of chromosome structure at this stage.

When the spores are stained with toluidine blue, a tightly knit group of metachromatic granules can be seen lodged alongside the nucleus. The significance of this striking re-action is unfortunately unknown, and the best we can do is surmise that this represents a group of polysaccharide par-ticles of unknown function. In the other stages of the life cycle, except the stage of active feeding where metachromasia is totally absent, the granules are randomly distributed through the cytoplasm rather than in one closely integrated bunch.

From his electron micrographs Mühlethaler (1956) has been able to demonstrate clearly that the spore wall is made up of two layers, a double membrane. He believes that the outer one is condensed slime material of unknown chemical nature (similar to the slime sheath), while the inside wall is an intercrossed lacework of cellulose micelles which presum-ably give the spore its rigid framework. He points out that such a double membrane is common among micro-organisms, but as yet its significance is not fully appreciated.

A few hours after the spore is sown in a favorable environ-ment there is a split down the side of the capsule and the amoeba emerges. The process can be seen with considerable clarity in Arndt's motion picture. He used *D. mucoroides*, but the process of germination is the same in *D. discoideum*. The exact conditions which favor spore germination have not as yet been satisfactorily studied. It is presumed that a film of water over the spore is necessary, but there is conflicting evidence from various authors, starting with Brefeld, con-cerning the effect of humidity, the optimum temperature, or the effect of the chemical constitution of the medium.[1] From

[1] Especially noteworthy are the detailed studies of Potts (1902) on germination of *D. mucoroides* as well as those of Skupienski (1920). Yet despite these and other investigations a comprehensive study is still needed.

many such studies on fungi and other forms it is well known that there can be a complex interplay of these factors. It is well established that germination can occur in the absence of bacteria, although there may be no subsequent growth of the emerging amoeba.

6. The vegetative stage of *D. discoideum*

Another unfortunate gap in our knowledge is in the nuclear behavior of the vegetative amoebae. As mentioned previously, I have observed a few vegetative divisions and was able to find the haploid number of seven chromosomes. The difficulty is that the bacterial food supply picks up the nuclear stains avidly, and many hundreds of amoeba have to be examined critically before it is possible to find one that is, with any certainty, in the process of division. The matter is especially tantalizing because of the curious report of Olive (1902) that the first nuclear divisions following spore germination in *D. mucoroides* are rather special and, according to him, perhaps different from the subsequent divisions. This, of course, is quite possibly erroneous, but it should be checked along with many other details of the nuclear behavior.

Other cytological studies of vegetative amoebae have not revealed any very startling facts, with the possible exception of the absence of metachromasia mentioned previously. This presumably has some connection with the feeding process, but the nature of the connection is unknown. Another point of interest that has turned up in some preparations is that it is not uncommon to find evidences of cannibalism, a phenomena well known among amoebae in general. In some instances it is possible to see more than one amoeba inside another; in one case I have observed three amoebae, clearly within food vacuoles, inside one large cannibal. This observation is relevant to those of Wilson (1952, 1953; Wilson and Ross, 1957), who interprets one amoeba surrounding another as fertilization. That the cases mentioned above were cannibalism and not syngamy is borne out by two facts: 1) that more than one amoeba was inside the other (although this could be argued to be polyspermy), and 2) that the nuclei of the ingested amoebae are shown in various stages of digestion. One case has been observed of an amoeba in an aggregation stream with another partially digested amoeba inside it.

Another cytological detail worth mentioning is that, under a phase microscope and with Bodian's silver impregnation method, I have observed a polar cap on the nucleus (Plates V, VII). In some instances in the silver impregnation slides it is possible to see a strand extending out into the cytoplasm. The significance of these structures is unknown.

Besides the food vacuole there are one or more conspicuous contractile vacuoles which continually empty into the exterior. These vacuoles are present, as well, in the aggregative and migration stages and can be seen easily in living preparations.

The size range of the cells is greatest during the vegetative stage. If the cells are rounded up by placing them in a drop of standard salt solution, it is possible to measure the diameters (Bonner and Frascella, 1953); they range from about 5.5 μ to 16.0 μ, which in volume gives roughly over a twenty-fold difference between the smallest and largest vegetative cells. This matter was also checked using the more reliable method of measuring the diameters of the nuclei stained by the Feulgen method (Fig. 4), where a range was found between 2.6 and 5.2 μ, an eight-fold difference in volume between the smallest and largest nuclei (Bonner, Chiquoine, and Kolderie, 1955).

The amoebae are normally dependent on bacteria for their nutrition. These they engulf by phagocytosis and retain in food vacuoles during the digestive period. There is in the early literature considerable confusion concerning the role of the bacteria, and the matter was finally and completely straightened out by the analysis of Raper (1939). With increasing interest in experimental work on these organisms, there has been a great need to culture the amoebae in the absence of

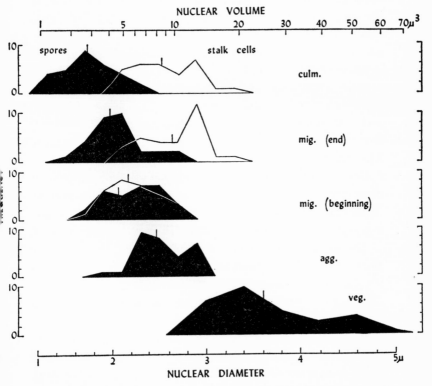

Fig. 4. The distribution of nuclear size measured at different stages of development in *Dictyostelium discoideum*. Each sample is based on the measurement of thirty nuclei. *Culm*, culmination; *mig*, migration; *agg*, aggregation. (From Bonner, Chiquoine, and Kolderie, 1955.)

bacteria on a purely chemical medium, preferably of a known composition. Some progress has been achieved in this direction with the discovery by Potts (1902), confirmed by Raper (1937), that the amoebae would grow on dead bacteria; the work of Bradley and Sussman (1952) further showed that they could obtain some growth with a medium of partially known composition. The unknown was a bacterial extract which they were able subsequently to characterize as a protein fraction (Sussman and Bradley, 1954). There remains, however, much to be done on this problem, for not only is the growth reported by Sussman and Bradley much inferior to that produced with bacteria, but also, after numerous attempts, we have been unable to obtain any growth on the medium in our laboratory. This apparently stems from the difficulty of correctly preparing the protein fraction, and it is hoped that easier, more readily reproducible methods will be devised.

An especially interesting result of the study of Sussman and Bradley is the suggestion that protein rather than glucose, which is also present in the medium, is the main energy source. They consider that the glucose might possibly play a role in initiating the polysaccharide synthesis that leads to the formation of the stalk and spore case at a later stage of development. Furthermore, Gregg and his co-workers (1954, 1956) have evidence that proteins provide energy for the manufacture of polysaccharides at these more advanced stages of development. This will be discussed later in more detail.

7. The aggregation stage of *D. discoideum*

It is especially difficult in dealing with the aggregation stage to confine myself in this chapter to the purely descriptive matter and separate this discussion from the problem of the mechanism of the oriented movement which is the subject of the next. Therefore the reader should be cautioned that the description of aggregation in this section is not complete.

The first problem that arises is determining the nature of the conditions necessary for the initiation of the aggregation stage. Many of the earlier workers (Potts, 1902; Oehler,

1922; von Schuckmann, 1924; Arndt, 1937) using *D. mucoroides* pointed out that the depletion of the bacterial food supply is a potent factor in the initiation of aggregation. Raper (1940b) has corroborated this for *D. discoideum* in various ways, such as adding fresh bacteria to the colony and in this way delaying aggregation. If bacteria are added and the amoebae diluted, Potts (1902) showed that the aggregation could be delayed indefinitely. Raper (1940b) has done this by transferring the amoebae to fresh suspensions of bacteria every thirty-six hours for an extended period.

Such an experiment shows that besides the depletion of the food, the concentration of the amoebae plays a role. If the amoebae are not diluted, they will aggregate despite added food; the latter will only delay the process. It can be shown that the time required for initiation of aggregation has a definite optimum, dependent upon the concentration of amoebae (Raper, 1940a; Bonner, 1947). If the amoebae are too dilute and therefore too widely scattered, there will be no aggregation, despite the depletion of the food supply.

Raper (1940b) also showed that a decrease in humidity and an increase in temperature and exposure to light cause the aggregation process to appear two to four hours sooner than in the controls. The effect of the increase in temperature is probably the direct result of the desiccating effect of such a temperature change (Bonner and Shaw, 1957).

There is a considerable period lasting from four to eight hours between the vegetative stage and the aggregation stage. The appreciation of this interphase has come recently, especially from the cytological studies in which it became obvious that the cells cease feeding and change their staining characteristics. A difference in staining properties between vegetative and aggregation amoebae was first noticed by Arndt (1937), who reports a dark refractile body, as revealed by iron haemotoxylin, that appears only during the later stages.

I am in doubt as to what this corresponds to in our studies, but there are certainly differences in staining between the two stages. The most striking is the reappearance of the metachromatic granules during this interphase period. First a few and then progressively more cells will show this property, and we were able to demonstrate that metachromasia appeared before the production of or the sensitivity to the chemotactic substance acrasin.

Another obvious difference is the progressive disappearance of the food vacuoles. It is interesting to note that if the cells are centrifuged free of bacteria at any point in their vegetative phase, or if they are centrifuged during the interphase or when aggregation has already begun, in each case there will be an induced interphase period of six to eight hours before aggregation begins. Apparently the trauma of centrifugation brings the cells, irrespective of the stage, to the beginning of a new interphase period. The vegetative cells have, of course, now become deprived of bacteria, therefore it is understandable that they should enter the interphase. The cytological changes during this induced interphase appear to be the same as those of a normal interphase.

Another striking change that occurs in the interphase is a radical decrease in cell size. The mean diameter of an actively feeding vegetative cell is about 11 μ, while the mean of an aggregating cell is 7 μ (Bonner and Frascella, 1953). This great difference is no doubt accounted for largely by the fact that during the interphase period when feeding ceases, there is a gradual disappearance of the many food vacuoles. By the more accurate method of measuring the size of the nuclei, it is found that the vegetative nuclei have an average diameter of 3.6 μ, and the aggregating nuclei, 2.5 μ, indicating that the nucleus during aggregation averages two thirds the volume of the nucleus of the vegetative amoeba (Fig. 4).

At the end of the interphase period the cells become more

elongate; this change is a striking one noted by many of the early workers. The pattern of the first signs of aggregation will depend to a great extent both on the concentration of the amoebae over the substratum and the amount of water about the amoebae. If the amoebae are under water they frequently will first form large sweeping streams that extend 2 or 3 cm. or more without any real center. They soon break up into the more usual pattern of small centers, starting with a mere four or five amoebae and eventually spreading to an area ½ cm. in diameter. Initially, the amoebae come in separately, directly to the center, but very soon they tend to flow together into streams. From Arndt's (1937) time lapse motion pictures of *D. mucoroides* and Bonner's (1944) of *D. discoideum*, it is evident that the amoebae rarely flow in smoothly but usually aggregate in pulses. That is, there is a wave of fast inward motion that spreads outward like the ripple produced by a stone tossed into a still pond.

Recently, Shaffer (1956 et seq.) has examined the aggregation process in great detail and made many new and valuable observations. Most of them bear on the mechanism (including an interpretation of the possible significance of the pulsations) and therefore will be dealt with in more detail in the next chapter, although one observation is pertinent here. Earlier workers noted that the cells at some moments appear to fuse in a stream and at other moments, separate. Shaffer finds that the amoebae can exist in two main phases; in one phase they adhere to one another little or not at all, and in the other they adhere strongly. Those in the second phase (which represents a more advanced stage of development), may be said to be "integrated," to use Shaffer's term. Frequently an integrated stream of cells will spontaneously break up or "disintegrate," only to reaggregate and reintegrate elsewhere. Arndt (1937) makes the point that centers may often begin their formation and then dissolve, and

Shaffer not only concurs but finds that the normal process of development frequently involves a series of successive stages of integration and disintegration, integration finally taking ascendency in the formation of a pseudoplasmodium. The haphazard nature of this backward and forward progression emphasizes, according to Shaffer, the instability of this primitive associative development; it is as though the process of integration–disintegration teeters delicately on a fulcrum, the advantage on the integration side sometimes being very slight indeed.

Some consideration has been given to the interesting problem of the polarity of the amoebae during aggregation (Bonner, 1950). As is well known, amoebae in general have a permanently identifiable posterior foot region, and the amoeba of *D. discoideum* is no exception. If, then, a center is removed and placed behind an aggregating amoeba, it will not simply back up, but will turn around and flow toward the center in its new location. If a section of a large stream is removed and turned about 180°, it will round up and disintegrate, to use Shaffer's term, and the separate amoebae will stream toward the center. If, on the other hand, the piece that is rotated 180° is attached to or grafted onto the cut stump of the stream leading into the center, then there will be no disintegration. The piece will round up to some extent and appear to be drawn out in the direction of the center. The stickiness has been retained and the disoriented piece pulled into the center. What happens to the orientation of the individual amoebae within the cohesive mass is unfortunately not known.

Occasionally the aggregation streams do not come toward a solid center, but form a whirlpool, giving rise to a center shaped like a doughnut (Arndt, 1937; Raper, 1941b). Shaffer also has studied these rings and finds that in some species they occur under certain cultural conditions with considerable frequency; furthermore, they can be constructed artificially by pushing the cells of aggregation streams into circles. These rings may continue to chase their tails around and around for many hours, the central hole sometimes expanding, sometimes contracting. Eventually each one condenses into a solid mass, a central tip appears if the mass is big enough and a normal fruiting body results.

In the studies of the staining properties of the aggregation amoebae it was noticed that stains specific for polysaccharides revealed a concentration on one side of the nucleus (Bonner, Chiquoine, and Kolderie, 1955). However, in aggregation patterns this concentration is not oriented with respect to the center; part of the time the mass will be posterior to the nucleus and part of the time, anterior. The same is true of the polar cap of the nucleus. Neither of these stainable bodies appears to be related to the polarity induced by aggregation.

Going from the histochemical to the purely biochemical approach, there have been a number of studies using inhibitors on aggregation (Hirschberg and Rusch, 1950, 1951; Hirschberg and Merson, 1955; Hirschberg, 1955; Takeuchi and Tazawa, 1955; Kostellow, 1956; Bradley, Sussman, and Ennis, 1956). As Takeuchi and Tazawa point out, there is some evidence to support the notion that the energy of movement during aggregation is furnished by oxidative phosphorylation. Kostellow, as well as Bradley, Sussman, and Ennis, studied the effects of amino acids and their analogues and found some that are remarkably specific. Of particular interest is the discovery within the latter group that histidine will increase the sensitivity of the amoebae so that they will aggregate when spread out sparsely over the surface of the agar, at a density which ordinarily would never permit aggregation.

During the interphase period before aggregation there are at first very few and finally no cell divisions (Bonner and

Frascella, 1952). Unfortunately, this information is confined to the interphase induced by centrifugation, for the normal interphase is obscured by the presence of bacteria. This absence of mitoses continues until the latter part of aggregation, and then some divisions appear, first in the apical papilla that rises above the agar, and finally in the whole mass during migration. However, there is a demonstrable difference in the distribution of mitoses in the front (pre-stalk) and hind (pre-spore) regions, which we suggested might reflect an early sign of differentiation. These observations, along with those of Wilson (1952, et seq.), emphasize the fact that the previous supposition that all cell division ceases at the aggregation phase is incorrect, and that aggregation only separates the feeding from the non-feeding, morphogenetic stages. These divisions are not especially numerous, the maximum being about one division per 100 cells for a short period immediately following aggregation, falling to one per 200 after ten hours of migration (Bonner and Frascella, 1952). Unfortunately, the duration of mitosis is not known, and therefore it is impossible to estimate within a pseudoplasmodium the total percent of the cells that have divided.

There are a number of points of sharp disagreement between our work and that of Wilson. He concludes that there are seven chromosomes and we suggested four, with seven arms. Labudde (1956) concurs with Wilson and seven is no doubt correct.[2] Whether arms or whole chromosomes, the number is uneven, which means that this is the haploid complement.

Another difference between our findings and Wilson's is

[2] Skupienski (1920) also states four chromosomes, but his illustrations are such that his conclusion has little weight. He did not have the advantage of orcein smears. Olive (1902) shows three chromosomes in his figures, but again no significance can be atached to this observation. Both of these authors worked with *D. mucoroides*, but seven is known to be the number there also.

that we interpreted the chromosome figures to be mitotic, and he interprets them as meiotic. This brings up the whole subject of his and Skupienski's (1920) views on sexuality in the Acrasiales, which will be briefly discussed.

As previously mentioned, both authors have suggested, contrary to the negative evidence of all other workers, that amoebae fuse in pairs at the onset of aggregation, and that meiosis appears subsequently in the pseudoplasmodium.[3] Aggregation is, according to Wilson, the diplophase. In Skupienski's scheme the aggregate is made up entirely of zygotes which then undergo two reduction divisions so that each zygote nucleus gives rise to four haploid spores. Wilson also states that "aggregation may be looked upon as a congregation of individuals, and each individual carries on the process of syngamy and meiosis according to the time of its arrival." In Wilson's scheme there are two meiotic divisions during and immediately following aggregation, and then two divisions just prior to stalk formation, so that each zygote produces sixteen spores.

It is possible now to state that both these proposed cycles are probably incorrect, and sexuality remains, as before, undemonstrated. There are many points in which the above cycles are inconsistent with the observations of other workers, as has been discussed by Sussman (1955b, 1956b), Raper (1956a), and Shaffer (1958).

In the first place the process of aggregation has been examined in living preparations for many hours by numerous workers (especially by Shaffer), and no one has seen cell fusions occurring at the moment of aggregation.

Another difficulty arises when Wilson proposes that cells

[3] Skupienski (1920) further argues for a plasmodial stage, but in this he stands entirely alone. The evidence from sectioned material, as well as many other observations, has definitely ruled this out. The only stage that still needs careful study is that of the macrocysts found in some strains of *D. mucoroides* (Blaskovics and Raper, 1957).

of large size are zygotes. From studies on cell and nuclear sizes (Bonner and Frascella, 1953; Bonner, Chiquoine, and Kolderie, 1955) it is obvious that this is likely to be misleading, for not only is the size–frequency distribution continuous and not bimodal, but also it extends over a considerable range.

Perhaps the most cogent argument against the above two sexual schemes is that, if one takes into account the time and number of meiotic divisions proposed during the cycle, then it can be shown that certain fruiting bodies of small cell number could not form as in fact they do. Sussman (1955a) produced a small mutant of *D. discoideum* in which he has obtained individuals of twelve cells of which there were nine spores. According to Skupienski's scheme, this would have consisted of three cells at the aggregation stage (not confirmed by Sussman), and according to Wilson's scheme there would have to be ¾ of a cell at aggregation (Plate VIII).

Another argument against the propositions of Skupienski and Wilson is genetic and comes from Sussman (1956b). He has made a long series of attempts to demonstrate recombination, bringing together different mutants at different stages in the life cycle, but he has met with no success. He points out that there are a number of possible difficulties, such as the slime molds being heterothallic, and his failing to bring the right mating types together. But this is far removed from the contentions of Skupienski and Wilson that aggregation is always a sexual phenomenon. This most assuredly is not necessarily the case, as is apparent from a critical examination. The idea that there might be some form of sexuality in the Acrasiales cannot, of course, be excluded, but we are little further in demonstrating such a possibility than we were back at the turn of the century. More recently Wilson and Ross (1957) have appeared with some further cytological observations. The suggestion that all the pre-aggregation cells are not gametes and all the aggregating cells are not zygotes is admitted as a possibility, relegating the sexual process to an occasional fusion between cells. The evidence, unfortunately, is no more compelling than in the earlier work, except for the demonstration of a few cells with fourteen chromosomes (also observed by Labudde, 1956). This is indeed an interesting point, although there are numerous alternative explanations other than sexuality which must be ruled out before the existence of sexuality can be rigorously established. Negative evidence is always unsatisfactory, and it is hoped that future genetic and cytological work will shed further light on this intriguing problem.

8. The migration stage of *D. discoideum*

One of the reasons that *D. discoideum* attracted such attention was the fact that it was the first cellular slime mold shown to have a stalkless migration period. The possibility of making grafts and performing various kinds of cutting experiments was immediately recognized and exploited by Raper with great profit. It has turned out, since, that many of these experiments can be performed with stalked forms, but *D. discoideum* showed the way. Raper (1956b) has since discovered another species with a stalkless migration period, but *D. polycephalum* is as yet too new to have made any contribution as experimental material.

Again, as with aggregation, the details of the movement must wait for the next chapter, but here let me say briefly that where the aggregating streams merge, the rising cone-shaped center turns directly into a migrating pseudoplasmodium. This now leaves the site of its formation by a slow, gliding movement. Sometimes the tip lies flat along the agar, while at other moments it may be raised, and it was noticed (Bonner, 1944) that when touching the substratum the tip would move more slowly, but when free in the air it would shoot forward; it resembles the human tongue in its ability to assume different shapes (Figs. 3, 12; Plate II).

During this stage the cell mass deposits a thin slime sheath which, like a collapsed sausage casing, lies flat on the surface of the substratum behind the advancing pseudoplasmodium. From the histological work there is no evidence that any particular group of cells, either near the surface or at the interior, is responsible for secreting this slime sheath. Therefore, it has been presumed to be exuded by all the amoebae, perhaps in some manner such as Paddock (1953) has demonstrated for the individual vegetative amoebae, although it is more likely associated with the stickiness exhibited by aggregating amoebae. It can be easily shown by plunging a migrating mass under the surface of some water, that probably the slime sheath is thinnest at the anterior end, for the cells will disengage themselves from the mass first in that region in the unfavorable aqueous environment. It can also be shown that the slime track itself does not move, but that the amoebae move within it. This may be readily done by placing a marker on the surface of the sheath (either carbon black or *Lycopodium* spores); the marker will retain a fixed position, while the pseudoplasmodium will slip out from under as it moves forward.

There have been some attempts to identify the slime sheath material chemically, but this has proven difficult because of its extreme thinness. Using staining techniques for cellulose, Raper and Fennell (1952) suggests that the slime sheath is made up partly of cellulose and partly of mucin. The evidence for cellulose comes from a positive reaction with chloroiodide of zinc, although Schweitzer's reagent does not destroy the slime track as it would were it pure cellulose. But these authors found that the birefringence, which is normally demonstrable under polarized light, is obliterated by the Schweitzer's reagent. However, the more recent electron microscope study of Mühlethaler (1956) shows that there are no fibrils in the sheath, which he interprets as positive evidence for the complete absence of cellulose.

In general, in the stained sections of the migrating stage the cells are somewhat rounded, lacking the elongate orientation characteristic of the aggregation stage. There is evidence of pseudopods, often interlocking between cells, but they are ordinarily not extended to any marked degree. The exception to this usual picture is at the very beginning of migration. Frequently at that stage, the cells can be seen to form a whirlpool or some kind of curved orientation within the mass. Also in some cases where there is a narrow tapering apex of an early migrating pseudoplasmodium, the cells will show elongation in a transverse direction, perpendicular to what must have been the axis of thrust. This orientation is seen again in the culmination stage (Figs. 3, 12; Plate VII).

One of the principal objects of the various histological studies was to detect early signs of cell differentiation, for it was known from the grafting experiments of Raper (1940b) that the anterior end of the migrating mass gives rise to the stalk cells, and the posterior end gives rise to the spore cells. He showed this by growing *D. discoideum* on the red bacterium *Serratia marcescens*, and since the amoebae retained the pigment prodigiosin, it was possible to obtain red pseudoplasmodia. Then by grafting a red anterior onto a white posterior migrating mass (and vice-versa), he was able to follow the fates of the different regions; in the words of the experimental embryologist, he mapped out their prospective significance.

In some early studies using haematoxylin, it was easy to see that at the beginning stages of migration there was no difference in staining properties between the anterior and posterior cells, but at a later stage the two regions were clearly identifiable and were separated by a sharp division line (Bonner, 1944). The differences were of two sorts; the posterior cells stained more darkly with the haematoxylin, and the posterior cells were smaller than the anterior cells.

The size difference has been pursued both by directly measuring the cell diameter in living preparations (Bonner and Frascella, 1953) and by the more satisfactory method of measuring the diameters of nuclei which have been prepared by the Feulgen method (Bonner, Chiquoine, and Kolderie, 1955). In a late migration stage the mean diameter of the posterior cells (having rounded up by being separated and placed in a standard salt solution) is 7.7μ, while that of the anterior cells is 8.5μ; the difference between the two is statistically highly significant despite the great overlap of their ranges. In the study on nuclear size, there was no demonstrable difference between the front and hind cells at the beginning of migration; both had a mean diameter of approximately 2.1μ. But in a late migrating pseudoplasmodium the posterior cells had a mean of 1.9μ and the anterior cells a mean of 2.6μ; again, despite the large range, these differences are highly significant. One further point here is of considerable interest. As can be seen from Fig. 4, at the beginning of migration the cells in the posterior region (the presumptive spore cells) have smaller nuclei than those of the aggregating cells, and the nuclei of late-migration presumptive spores are still smaller. In fact, a glance at the whole figure shows a continuous decrease in size from the vegetative stage to the encapsulated spores. The presumptive stalk cells, on the other hand, show an increase in nuclear size at late migration; therefore, the difference that appears between the two regions during the migration stage is due in part to a decrease in the size of the nuclei of the posterior presumptive spores, but to an even greater extent to the swelling of the anterior presumptive stalk nuclei.

The difference in the staining reaction of the two regions with haematoxylin could not, however, be accounted for by the change in cell size. The presumptive spore cells contained small, round, deeply-stained granules that were totally absent in the presumptive stalk cells. Still another difference in the staining properties was discovered quite by accident. It was found that a number of vital dyes, Bismarck brown, neutral red, Nile blue sulphate, and even the prodigiosin of *Serratia marcescens*, would produce, at first, a uniformly colored migrating pseudoplasmodium, and then at a later stage the anterior end would remain dark while the posterior end blanched, thus giving a vital demonstration of the two presumptive regions (Bonner, 1952). The dye was incorporated into the amoebae at the vegetative stage, the excess washed free by centrifugation, and the stained amoebae placed on non-nutrient agar so that aggregation and migration could follow. The blanching of the posterior end was recorded by time lapse photography, and it was possible to show that the change took place rapidly in a matter of ten to fifteen minutes. This rapid change excluded the idea that there had been a movement of the dye from one part of the pseudoplasmodium to another, and indicated, rather, that there must have been a change in the condition of the dye in the cells to give this blanching. Another argument in favor of an alteration of the dye within the cells comes from cutting experiments, in which an all-blanched segment will produce a new dark tip, and an all-dark segment will produce a blanched posterior end. These coloration changes are therefore strictly reversible. The only unfortunate part of this story is that we have no idea, as yet, of the nature of this dye change. The fact that so many different dyes show the effect would suggest that there is some sort of non-specific clumping phenomenon of the dye particles, but there is no evidence on this point.

With the idea of obtaining some further insight into the

differences between the presumptive stalk and presumptive spore areas, a program was launched using some of the more modern histochemical techniques (Bonner, Chiquoine, and Kolderie, 1955). A number of different methods were tried, but two in particular produced rewarding results.

Perhaps the most successful is the periodic acid-Schiff reaction for polysaccharides.[4] The vegetative and the aggregation amoebae show numerous granules containing polysaccharide, and at the end of aggregation the cell mass stains homogeneously. As migration proceeds, the division line between pre-stalk and pre-spore is sharply delineated by this PAS reaction. The posterior pre-spore cells are now laden with numerous small, darkly pigmented, buckshot-like granules. These correspond closely with the granules revealed by haematoxylin, indicating that the differences between the two regions demonstrated by the earlier haematoxylin studies were differences in the non-starch polysaccharides. These differences become even more exaggerated as culmination follows.

During the migration phase the PAS preparations show a small wedge of cells at the very posterior end of the mass. These cells show the staining characteristics of the anterior pre-stalk cells. Furthermore, it is obvious that some of these rear-guard cells keep falling behind and may be observed in the slime track, where they cease all forward movement and appear somewhat vacuolate. As will be shown in the discussion of culmination, there is considerable evidence indicating that these rear-guard cells give rise to the basal disc.

The second method that revealed differences was one designed to show the presence of alkaline phosphatase, and our results have been independently confirmed by Krivanek (1956). In early migration the cell mass stains fairly uniformly except for a small darkly pigmented patch at the

[4] The preparations were digested in saliva, therefore we were staining primarily for the non-starch polysaccharides.

anterior tip. This area of high alkaline phosphatase activity progressively enlarges so that the whole pre-stalk area is distinct after a period of migration. This reaction also intensifies during the culmination stage, and the interpretation of these results, as well as those of the polysaccharides, may most appropriately be discussed along with the general problems of culmination.

9. The culmination stage of *D. discoideum*

At the end of migration the tip of the cell mass ceases movement while the posterior portion continues to gather in, thereby causing the pseudoplasmodium to round up. The hind end shoves itself under the main mass, and the principal axis now becomes vertical (Fig. 3). The whole mass then flattens itself on the surface of the substratum, as the motion pictures and time interval photographs show, only to rise again soon and continue its upward movement, the actual culmination. As it does this, the presumptive spore mass is pulled away from the surface of the substratum and lifted into the air; the apical papilla of presumptive stalk cells also rises, sometimes smoothly, but more often in throbbing pulsations. This papilla of pre-stalk cells slowly diminishes in size until finally the spherical or more often lemon-shaped sorus lies at the tip of the delicately tapering stalk (Plates III, IV).

If these changes are followed internally, primarily with the use of stained sections (Bonner, 1944), then it is possible to see the exact fate of the two cell types. The presumptive stalk cells first turn into true stalk cells in the apical region by a rounded group of cells becoming vacuolated. Further stalk cells are continuously added to the group from above, in this way pushing the first-formed mature stalk cells downward like a wedge towards the substratum, right through the cell mass. The fact that this occurs, rather than the stalk cells arising *in situ* up and down the main axis, which had been the suggestion of earlier workers, was conclusively proved using Raper's (1940b) technique of grafting a red pseudo-plasmodium tip onto a white posterior portion (Bonner, 1952). In this particular preparation I was fortunate to be able to see clearly that the initial stalk cells were entirely red, and were pushed down through the white pre-spore cells (Fig. 5). The flattening of the whole mass, mentioned above, occurs when the new stalk is pushing its way down; when it reaches the substratum it meets with some resistance for the first time, and now the piling of the presumptive stalk cells on top of the rigid stalk (by a reverse-fountain movement) results in the rising of the pre-stalk and pre-spore mass.

Around the base of the stalk there are the rear-guard cells which we noted have pre-stalk polysaccharide staining characteristics. These cells now become vacuolated and directly produce the basal disc. As the pre-spore mass rises, there may be some remaining rear-guard cells attached at its posterior end, indicating either that all of them did not become basal disc cells, or that they accumulated in that region after the formation of the basal disc.

From the histological sections it is clear that final spore differentiation begins on the upper edge of the pre-spore mass and progresses inward and downward from that region. There is a mild controversy as to whether this occurs quickly (Bonner, 1944) or slowly (Raper and Fennell, 1952). My evidence is based entirely on the correlation between the appearance of opacity of the sorus in motion pictures and serial photographs, and the final encapsulation of the spores as revealed in stained paraffin sections; if the correlation is sound, then the process occurs in less than an hour. The discrepancy between our views might be caused by the presence of the rear-guard cells which do not differentiate into spores.

To return to the matter of stalk formation, there are a number of further points worth considering. The stalk sheath itself is a cylinder of cellulose that lies outside the cell walls of the stalk cells proper (Raper and Fennell, 1952).[5] There is a delicate taper to the stalk, and the problem of what factors

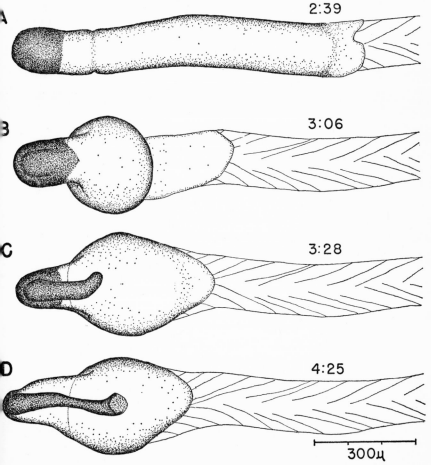

Fig. 5. Camera lucida drawings (surface view) showing how the stalk is first formed at the tip and is pushed downward through the pre-spore cells to the substratum. The dark tip was obtained by grafting the tip of a colored migrating cell mass onto a decapitated colorless one. (From Bonner, 1952.)

[5] This can be seen particularly well in an electron micrograph of Gezelius and Rånby (1956, Fig. 10).

govern this taper has been raised by Harper (1926), who imagined that the decreasing weight of the sorus caused by a pressure stimulus would affect the diameter of the stalk. There are many objections to such a notion, one being that a tapered stalk will form in inverted cultures where the fruiting bodies are pointing downward. The more reasonable view is that expressed by Raper and Fennell (1952) that the mass of pre-stalk cells diminishes as culmination proceeds, and that the progressive taper comes with the reduction of the diameter of the pre-stalk mass. This matter of taper, as the observations of Pfützner-Eckert (1950) on the taper of *D. mucoroides* indicate, remains an unsolved problem of considerable interest.

The question of what group of cells contributes the stalk material was answered by our studies with the polysaccharide stain. The pre-stalk cells, as was well known, become elongate and line up with their long axis approximately perpendicular to the stalk axis. The inner portion of these cells is extremely rich in non-starch polysaccharide, giving a clear indication that they are actively secreting the stalk sheath. The actions of any particular pre-stalk cell then have the following sequence. As the cell rises into the upper portion of the papilla, it elongates and becomes a part of a transitory columnar epithelium. After secreting its polysaccharide as a contribution to the stalk sheath, it passes up to the tip and becomes incorporated into the stalk proper. By a gradual process of enlargement it becomes vacuolated and finally secretes its own cellulose cell wall.

The fact that the stalk sheath consists of cellulose was first suggested by Brefeld (1869). This was supported by the work of Olive (1902) and Raper (1940a), but the first comprehensive attack on the problem is that of Raper and Fennell (1952). By the use of chemicals as well as X-ray defraction studies, paper chromatography of hydrolysis products, and decomposition by cellulose-destroying bacteria, they established the cellulose nature of the stalk sheath beyond question. The X-ray diffraction patterns were those of a hydrate cellulose, and this and other points were corroborated by studies of Mühlethaler (1956). Furthermore, Mühlethaler showed with electron micrographs that the fibrils in the sheath are beautifully oriented in a parallel fashion, while the fibrils in the walls of the stalk cells are oriented at random. The diameter of the fibrils is the same for the stalk sheath, the stalk cells, and the spore casing: about 70-100 Å, which is, according to Mühlethaler, thinner than the fibrils of the cells of higher plants. In a recent paper Gezelius and Rånby (1957) agree, for the most part, with these observations, although they consider the cellulose to be partly mercerized.

When the cells first enter the stalk proper, they are small, but as newly arrived cells pile on top of them they expand rapidly. It is impossible, because of the irregular shape of the cells, to make an accurate estimate of cell volume and therefore gauge the extent of this increase in volume. Furthermore, in this instance our studies on the nuclear size were of no help, because apparently the increase in cell size is not accompanied by a corresponding change in the nucleus. There is, in fact, no appreciable change in the nuclear size between the pre-stalk cells at the end of migration and the young stalk cells (Fig. 4). When vacuolization of the stalk cells becomes pronounced at about the level of the center of the spore mass, then the nuclei become irregular and crinkled and no longer appear healthy. This suggests that mature stalk cells are for all intents and purposes dead cells.

In the histochemical study, as was mentioned earlier, the pre-spore cells show increasing concentration of non-starch polysaccharide, until finally the cellulose spore capsule shows an intense coloration with a number of large granules inside.[6]

[6] These internal granules are very likely to be granules that appear metachromatic when stained with toludin blue.

At all times the presumptive stalk cells are fainter in this poly-saccharide reaction, even when they are exuding the stalk material or manufacturing their own cellulose wall inside the stalk sheath.

Both in our studies (Bonner, Chiquoine, and Kolderie, 1955) and the studies of Krivanek (1956), the pre-stalk cells show a relatively high alkaline phosphatase activity, and this becomes increasingly intense, especially in the lower regions, below the zone of stalk deposition. Also, the rear-guard cells show a strong reaction during culmination, a fact that is especially striking in some of Krivanek's photographs. Fur-thermore, Krivanek made a most interesting original observa-tion that was missed by us, namely: that the actual process of spore encapsulation is accompanied by a wave of intense alkaline phosphatase activity.

On the purely biochemical level Krivanek (1956) made colorimetric analyses of the alkaline phosphatase and found that there was no significant difference between the vegetative and migrating amoebae in total quantity, but that there was a sharp increase during culmination. The mature sorocarps were very low in alkaline phosphatase.

A somewhat different and most interesting biochemical approach has been launched by Gregg and his group. Gregg, Hackney, and Krivanek (1954) have shown that during culmination there is a reduction of protein nitrogen com-ponents, and Gregg and Bronsweig (1956a and b) have evidence for an increase in reducing substances (presumably carbohydrates). From this Gregg suggests that carbohydrates are synthesized from protein during the morphogenetic stages, indicating that the carbohydrate reserves stored during the vegetative period are insufficient for the complete fruiting process. This information fits well with the observation of Sussman and Bradley (1952, 1954) that protein is the main energy source even during the vegetative phase.

If we now try to put these various histo- and bio-chemical facts together, we are, I suppose, primarily impressed by the magnitude of our ignorance and the total inability to describe the development of the slime mold in any kind of a chemical epigenesis. Nevertheless, there are some striking facts which at least point the way for future work.

In the first place it should be remembered that the stalk which lifts the sorus into the air is a cylinder of cellulose. In the case of the spore cell also, we say it has differentiated when it has produced a smooth capsule-shaped wall. The substance, then, which is molded to give *Dictyostelium* its architectural form, its support, and its characteristic differentiation, is cellulose. Viewed in this light it is not surprising to find that one of the earliest signs of differentiation is a difference in the cellular distribution of polysaccharide. It should be mentioned parenthetically here, that by cutting experiments one can show that these polysaccharide changes of the cells are reversible, and that characteristically stained pre-stalk cells can be converted to characteristically stained pre-spore cells and vice-versa.

There is a major difference in the ultimate role of stalk and spore cells: the stalk dies, but before death it secretes the stalk sheath and then throws its depleted, hollow frame into the cavity of the sheath to become a brick in the supporting tower. The spore, on the other hand, saves its reserves behind a hard case, and, like a seed, it waits for favorable circumstances to propagate future generations of slime molds.

These changes in polysaccharide, we can presume from the work of Gregg and his co-workers, are the result of protein metabolism. The role of the alkaline phosphatase is more difficult to assess. Krivanek (1956) points out that it is correlated with both stalk formation in the pre-stalk cells and encapsulation in the spore cells, suggesting that it plays a role in the synthesis of cellulose. This possibility is indeed tempting, but

I feel it should be approached with caution, because, for instance, the zone of active stalk deposition does not correspond exactly with the zone of highest alkaline phosphatase. Nevertheless, the relation is still possible, and the biochemical work of the future will decide.

10. *Dictyostelium mucoroides* (*and D. purpureum*)

The justification for lumping these two species together in this general description of their characteristics is that, except for the purple color, the two forms are indistinguishable, and what can be said of one applies to the other (Fig. 6). The point has already been made that both show considerable variability among isolates or strains, this being especially obvious in the case of *D. mucoroides*, because it is more common and therefore more frequently isolated from nature. The most striking variation is in the general size of the fruiting bodies, and the fact that some species (usually the larger ones) have a long migration under ideal conditions, while others migrate for very brief periods and fruit directly. Some of the other differences among strains will be mentioned presently.

The process of aggregation and other characteristics of the life cycles of the cellular slime molds were studied in great detail by many of the earlier workers; these efforts were almost entirely confined to *D. mucoroides*. This includes the earlier observations of Brefeld (1869, 1884), and van Tieghem (1880). At the turn of the century Olive (1902) contributed to a further clarification of the problem, but the most remarkable experimental study is that of Potts (1902), who did much to gain insight into the physiological conditions of the development process. I will not, at this juncture, enter into a detailed analysis of Potts' experiments, but will refer to them

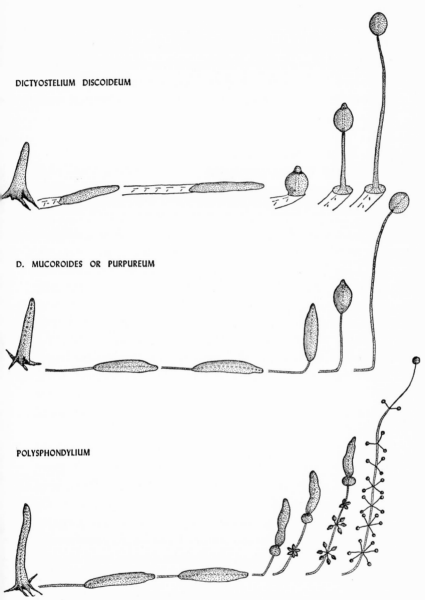

DICTYOSTELIUM DISCOIDEUM

D. MUCOROIDES OR PURPUREUM

POLYSPHONDYLIUM

Fig. 6. The migration and culmination stages of three different types of cellular slime mold. (From Bonner, 1958.)

in pertinent sections; the reason for this is that his paper is a mixture of facts, some known to be incorrect and others which are not only correct but showed great foresight on his part. In more recent years Harper (1926), Arndt (1937), Pfützner-Eckert (1950), and finally Shaffer (1956 et seq.) have studied various aspects of the development of this species.

The description already given for the aggregation of *D. discoideum* applies with no very radical alterations to the aggregation of *D. mucoroides* (and *D. purpureum*). One exception to this statement might be that in some strains of *D. mucoroides* there is a loose association of the amoebae over a large area before they break up into specific aggregation patterns (the "preplasmodium" stage of Arndt, 1937; see also Shaffer, 1957c). The next noticeable difference is at the end of aggregation: the conical, rising central mass begins to form a stalk even before the aggregation process is completed. In some instances the pseudoplasmodium will have lifted into the air, and a large aggregation stream runs along the stalk into the "sorogen," as Harper (1926) has called the rising cell mass. As migration proceeds, the stalk forms continuously, so that if the migration is extensive the sorus will be correspondingly small, for the amoebae have been used up in the manufacture of stalk (Fig. 6). The migration mass will touch the surface of the substratum either partially or in some cases not at all. There is evidence for slime sheath formation during the migration, as in *D. discoideum*, but the sheath is not readily visible behind, for it apparently collapses about the stalk.

Raper and Thom (1941) first showed that there are some strains of *D. purpureum* (and *D. mucoroides*) that periodically have short interruptions in the stalk formation process, leaving a series of gaps in the stalk. Both in Raper's and in our laboratory we found that under certain cultural conditions this situation may be exaggerated (and even produced in strains where it had not previously been observed). In general, those conditions which favor migration favor the interruption of the stalk, but the correlation is not perfect and further work is needed to settle the point.

It is profitable to apply the non-starch polysaccharide staining method (the PAS reaction) to *D. mucoroides* and *D. purpureum*, for the situation is somewhat different from that found in *D. discoideum* (Bonner, Chiquoine, and Kolderie, 1955; Bonner, 1957). In the first place, right at the end of aggregation it is possible to see a clear line of demarcation between the pre-stalk and pre-spore area (Fig. 7). There is no period of migration in which all the cells have the same staining characteristics; the beginning of the differentiation process occurs earlier in these forms. It is premature at this moment to discuss the matter of proportions between spore and stalk cells, but it is a striking and easily recognizable fact that the zone of presumptive stalk cells in *D. mucoroides* (and *D. purpureum*) is much smaller than the equivalent zone in *D. discoideum* (Fig. 7).

Normally in various strains of *D. mucoroides* tested, there was a distinct and clear zone of rear-guard cells at the posterior end of the sorogen, and it was possible to show that with increased migration the size of this zone increased. This was readily measurable, for the rear-guard cells have the same staining characteristics as the pre-stalk cells. An interesting exception to this was the case of a particular strain (Dm-4) which showed no rear-guard cells no matter how long the period of migration. From the studies on proportions there is reason to believe that the rear-guard cells in this strain simply had not accumulated at the posterior end, but were to be found throughout the pre-spore mass. There is, of course, no basal disc in *D. mucoroides*, and therefore the functional significance of these cells is obscure.

When spore differentiation takes place, the remaining pre-

Dictyostelium discoideum

D. mucoroides or purpureum

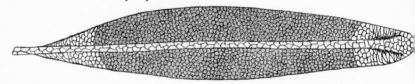

Polysphondylium

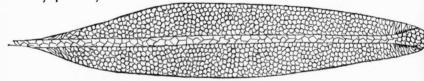

Fig. 7. The staining properties of the cells (using the periodic acid-Schiff method) during the migration phase for three different types of cellular slime molds. (From Bonner, 1958.)

stalk cells are used up in stalk formation and the fruiting process comes to an end. With one exception there has been no instance cited in the literature of the formation of spore cells except at the normal period at the end of a stalk. Numerous attempts have been made to induce separate amoebae to develop into true spores, but to no avail. The exception is the observation by Potts (1902) that if aggregation was allowed to take place under water, the resulting cell mass would produce spore cells in the absence of stalk cells. A possible explanation of this unique observation will be provided presently.

According to Blaskovics and Raper (1957), there are some strains of *D. mucoroides* that occasionally produce "microcysts." These are separate vegetative amoebae that become rounded up under unfavorable growth conditions and each produces a thin, firm wall (Fig. 8). According to Olive

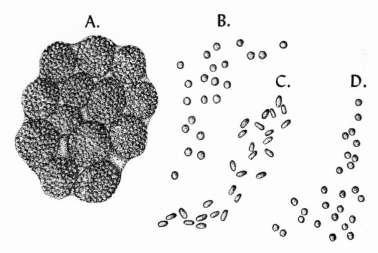

Fig. 8. Different types of resistant bodies of the Acrasiales. A, macrocysts; B, microcysts; and C, spores of *D. mucoroides*; D, spores of *D. Lacteum.*

(1902) this phenomenon was first discovered by Cienkowski for *Guttulina*, but Blaskovics and Raper have since discovered it not only in *D. mucoroides* but also in *D. minutum, D. polycephalum, Polysphondylium pallidum,* and *Acytostelium leptosomum.* Furthermore, they have carefully observed encystment and germination, and have come to the conclusion that the microcysts are true cysts, for upon germination it is possible to see the empty, hyaline shells.

Blaskovics and Raper (1957) have also described in great detail another structure which is produced by some strains of *D. mucoroides* and *D. minutum*. This is the "macrocyst," which consists of a condensed aggregate of cells that is surrounded by a thickened wall (Fig. 8). This was first observed by Raper a number of years ago, and he suggests that the "dwarfed sporangia" of Brefeld (1869) were most likely macrocysts.

In a careful examination of the role of macrocysts in the life cycle, Blaskovics and Raper (1957) come to the following conclusions. They form as the result of a small but normal aggregation; the aggregated mass, instead of heaping up and forming a stalk, rounds up into irregular spheres of cell masses, and each sphere becomes covered with a heavy cellulose wall. After a period the boundaries of the compressed, polyhedral cells within the macrocyst are no longer visible; this stage is followed by a contraction of the internal protoplasmic material. Blaskovics and Raper did not ascertain the nuclear and cellular nature of the protoplasm during these stages, but the evidence is excellent, pending histological and cytological studies, that these macrocysts do germinate and produce myxamoebae. The environmental conditions, especially the effect of temperature and the composition of the medium, were found to affect differentially the formation of normal fruiting bodies and spores as opposed to macrocysts. Even the conditions which favor germination of spores and macrocysts appear to differ, depending to some extent on the strain. They also were able to demonstrate that macrocysts are more resistant to adverse environmental conditions than myxamoebae, but not so resistant as true spores. From these facts Blaskovics and Raper suggest that possibly macrocysts represent an alternative resting stage; that is, in the species

D. mucoroides there may be three resistant bodies: micro-cysts, macrocysts, and true spores.

It occurred to me after reading Blaskovics and Raper's paper that perhaps the function of macrocysts might be an alternative resting stage particularly suited for underwater sporulation. Since normal spores cannot form underwater, yet aggregation does occur under these circumstances, it would indeed be advantageous to produce resting bodies, for in seasons of high rainfall it might be hard to find a suitably dry surface for normal development. When such a macrocyst strain was immersed under water, we soon found that beautiful clusters of macrocysts were produced in the bottom of the dish. Not only does this provide a possible explanation for the function of macrocysts, but it also suggests that the underwater spores of Potts (1902) might have been macrocysts.

Furthermore, it should be mentioned that Blaskovics and Raper showed that some strains which formed macrocysts could, by single cell isolation, be separated into clones which would differ in their ability to produce them. This will be considered again in the last chapter in the discussion of the cell variation within a strain. The only other species that produces macrocysts, according to these same authors, is *D. minutum.*

In observing *D. purpureum* Raper noticed that when this species grows in the presence of phenol it fails to develop the purple color but remains white. This was examined in detail by Whittingham and Raper (1956), and they found that the phenomenon was not a pH effect but was specifically produced by phenol and other related compounds. The white spores produced by the phenol are viable and produce normal purple offspring in the absence of phenol; there has been no permanent genetic alteration. They found this same effect on the purple color of *Polysphondylium violaceum.* They do not speculate on the biochemical mechanism, and indeed here, also, there is a need for further investigation. It would be surprising if the purple color were not found to be a melanin, the synthesis of which is interfered with in some way by the phenol compounds.

11. *Dictyostelium polycephalum*

This interesting species, recently discovered by Raper (1956b), has a number of features which mark it as quite different from other members of the genus (Fig. 9). A care-

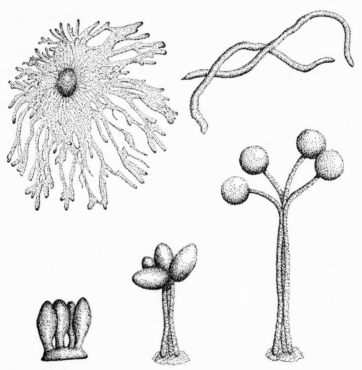

Fig. 9. *Dictyostelium polycephalum. Upper left*, an aggregation pattern; *upper right*, migrating pseudoplasmodia; *bottom*, progressive steps during culmination beginning with one pseudoplasmodium breaking up into a series of small fruiting bodies. (Drawings based primarily on photographs by Raper, 1956b.)

ful study of its life cycle has been made by Raper (1956b), and I shall indicate some of the principal points here.

To begin with, the germination process is unusual. Instead of a longitudinal split down the side of the elliptical spore case, the spore wall bulges out around the equator where it eventually bursts, liberating the protoplast and leaving either two separate or two partially attached, empty, hemispherical spore cases.

The vegetative stage of *D. polycephalum* is similar to that of other members of the Acrasiales, while the aggregation is different in that it lacks the conspicuous thin radiating streams; rather, there are broad sheets of cells that converge on the central collection points. Each of these central masses will give rise to as many as a dozen or more migrating pseudoplasmodia.

The migrating masses are stalkless as in *D. discoideum*, but here the similarity stops. They are extremely thin and long— up to 5 to 10 mm. in length and about 50 to 60 μ in diameter. These string-like masses have the further peculiarity of showing no tropisms to light and heat.

From some material kindly sent to us by Raper we made some periodic acid-Schiff preparations for non-starch polysaccharides of these migrating masses and found them to show no signs of early differentiation whatsoever. This is not surprising considering the nature of the subsequent development.

The migration process ceases when the pseudoplasmodium accumulates in one large globular mass; it then becomes subdivided into a series of one to nine papillae, each of which initiates stalk formation and rises as a fruiting body. As these culminate, their stalks fuse or lie alongside one another, cemented together for at least three quarters of their length, after which each stalk juts out, with a spherical sorus at its apex. The result is a coremiform fructification, in which there are a series of *D. discoideum*-like fruiting bodies (minus the basal discs), bound together along most of their stalks like a bunch of flowers in a narrow vase (Fig. 9). It would be most interesting to know if the point at which each individual fruiting body diverges from the mass is also the point at which final spore differentiation occurs. This would seem to me a reasonable possibility, because from this moment on, as a result of spore encapsulation, there would be a negligible production of the binding slime sheath material. This would also argue that the main cohesive force in bringing the stalks together is in the adhering sheath of each sorocarp.

The conditions which favor fructification in this particular species are somewhat different from those encountered in other forms (Whittingham and Raper, 1957). In the first place, the optimum fruiting temperature is about 30° C (with a maximum at 34°-35° C), while other species of *Dictyostelium* have an optimum closer to 22°-24° C and a maximum at approximately 30° C. Also it was found that *D. polycephalum* fruited with far greater frequency in a three-membered culture with a mold (*Dematium*) as well as the bacterial food supply (Raper, 1956b), and in the more recent study Whittingham and Raper were able to imitate the advantageous effect of the *Dematium* by slightly lowering the relative humidity of the atmosphere.

12. *Polysphondylium violaceum* and *P. pallidum*

The genus *Polysphondylium* is easily recognized by the whorls of branches that jut out from the mature sorocarp (Fig. 6). The common *P. violaceum* is a large and conspicuous form, although again there is considerable variation among isolates, especially as to the duration of migration (Bonner and Shaw, 1957). The less common, white-spored *P. pallidum* is much smaller and more delicate in its appearance. As is true of small species of Acrasiales in general (especially of *D. lacteum, D. minutum,* and *Acytostelium*), *P. pallidum* grows poorly on rich nutrient media and does best where the bacterial population is kept relatively low (Raper, 1951).

From spore germination to the early migration stage *Polysphondylium* is very similar in appearance to *D. mucoroides.* Shaffer (1957a) has pointed out some differences in the aggregation patterns, but the morphological changes are basically similar.

As migration proceeds, a group of cells is pinched off from the posterior end of the pseudoplasmodium, and this detached mass, which surrounds the stalk like a doughnut, subdivides into a series of small fruiting bodies that jut out at right angles from the stalk. The process is repeated many times, until finally the whole fruiting body has the appearance of a miniature Christmas tree with a sorus at the tip of each branch and one large terminal sorus at the end of the main stalk (Fig. 6).

Harper (1929, 1932) has made a detailed study of *Polysphondylium* and taken great pains to measure the number and distribution of whorls of a large number of fruiting bodies. On the basis of these measurements he argues for a fixity of structure, despite the great variation in size, that is, the number of whorls and the average number of branches per whorl are directly correlated with the size of the fruiting body. Also he found, as did Potts (1902) observing *D. mucoroides,* that the fruiting bodies of *Polysphondylium,* when grown in the light, were smaller than those raised in the dark. The difference, according to Harper (1932), is that the fruiting bodies in the dark had twenty-one per cent more whorls per plant and twenty-three per cent more branches.[7]

---

[7] These figures are in per cent of branched fruiting bodies only, discounting those that had no branches at all.

The effect of light in producing smaller plants is probably a general one for the Acrasiales, as Raper (1940b) points out, for it is found in *D. discoideum* and *D. mucoroides*. It is undoubtedly related to Raper's discovery that light induces aggregation to take place two to four hours sooner. Light therefore induces the early formation of small aggregates, but the mechanism is unknown.

If a histological analysis is made of the migrating cell mass of *Polysphondylium*, it is possible to see that it differs significantly from *D. mucoroides* (Bonner, Chiquoine, and Kolderie, 1955; Bonner, 1957). *Polysphondylium* is one of those species that produces a stalk which persists through the entire migration stage, yet there is absolutely no evidence of any division line between the pre-stalk and the pre-spore cells. All the cells except those that are either in the stalk or on the verge of entering it have a homogeneous non-starch polysaccharide distribution, showing staining properties similar to those of aggregating cells (Fig. 7).

This embryonic condition is sustained even after the groups of cells are cut off the posterior end prior to their formation of the whorl of branches. Repeated attempts were made to catch the moment when each small branch would show prestalk and pre-spore cells, but the stained sections either showed no differentiation or final differentiation of the spores; the transition period must be very short indeed.

The fact that *Polysphondylium* has such a radically different pattern of differentiation from *D. discoideum* and *D. mucoroides* argues strongly for the usefulness of the comparative method in the experimental analysis of these forms. For instance, we had presumed from the earlier work on *Dictyostelium* that no stalk could be produced without a pre-stalk zone, but *Polysphondylium* does this normally. There is, of course, also a sound rationalization as to why *Polysphondylium* has this delayed differentiation. After an extended period of migration the cell mass cuts off groups of cells at the posterior end and these groups further subdivide into what are essentially a cluster of small sorocarps. In this case the individual fruiting body with a single stalk and a single sorus does not become isolated from the communal cell mass until just before final differentiation. It is therefore not surprising that differentiation should wait until after the units are carved out. As a matter of fact, the same argument would apply to *Dictyostelium polycephalum*, for there, also, there is no differentiation during the migration stage, as was shown by the periodic acid-Schiff preparations, but only after the cell mass has broken up into the units that will be the final discrete fruiting bodies. In both cases there has been a prolongation of the embryonic characters, so that at a late moment the large cell mass can break up into smaller sub-units.

This property, which might be called a special slime mold form of neoteny, emphasizes the striking similarity between *Polysphondylium* and *D. polycephalum*, and suggests that the two might be closely allied. They differ primarily in the absence of the stalk during migration in *D. polycephalum*. The result is that when *D. polycephalum* breaks up into sub-units, it does so on the surface of the substratum rather than along a stalk as in *Polysphondylium*. Consequently, the fruiting body of *D. polycephalum* is one whorl jutting up from the surface of the substratum. It is true that *Polysphondylium* cuts off whorls at repeated intervals, and there is no equivalent for this in *D. polycephalum*. However, the fact that the doughnut-shaped cell mass does produce a whorl can probably be explained mechanically on the simple basis that it surrounds a cylindrical stalk, and the small fruiting bodies that are the branches tend to come off at right angles. In other words, both forms have the same mechanism of orientation of the fruiting bodies, since in *D. polycephalum* they come off at right angles from a flat substratum.

My argument, then, is that if a mutant of *Polysphondylium* arose that lacked the ability to form a stalk during migration, the immediate result might be *D. polycephalum*; it would be similar to a stalkless mutant of *D. mucoroides* giving rise to *D. discoideum*. Let me hasten to add, however, that I am not suggesting on the basis of this hypothesis that the generic name of *Dictyostelium polycephalum* should be changed. There are so few species in the Acrasiales that confusion is unlikely. It is true that Olive (1902) himself expressed doubts about the separation of *Dictyostelium* and *Polysphondylium*, the difference being based on whether the branches come off in whorls or not.[8] But since the names are easy and convenient as they now exist, let us not waste time with nomenclature, but instead seek a deeper understanding of the natures and relationships of these organisms.

13. *Acytostelium leptosomum*

This new species and genus of K. B. Raper (1956a; Raper and Quinlan, 1958) is of great interest, because it is the only cellular slime mold that produces a totally non-cellular stalk. The stalk is a very thin tube of cellulose bearing one round spore mass at its tip (Fig. 10).

The spores are spherical as in *D. lacteum*, and they germinate by a dissolution of part of the surface and a swelling of the protoplast. Once emerged, the amoebae resemble those of other Acrasiales, but as is true of other small and delicate species, they require a weak culture medium and are surprisingly rigid in their optimal culture requirements. Even when the growth and development is at its best, there is normally a large number of microcysts produced, which gives rise to an interesting source of confusion. The microcysts are spheri-

---

[8] Olive (1902, p. 508) says "it is possible that the distinction is not great enough to warrant the retention of the two forms as distinct genera."

cal and surrounded by a cellulose wall as are the spores, and according to Raper and Quinlan, their size range overlaps considerably (the microcysts are slightly larger on the average), and therefore it is impossible to decide whether any one

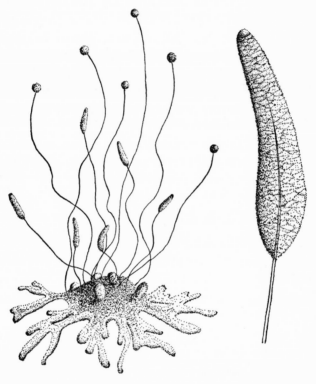

Fig. 10. *Acytostelium leptosomum. Left,* the simultaneous occurrence of aggregation and culmination; *right,* an enlarged culminating pseudoplasmodium showing the acellular stalk and the cell orientation. (Drawings based primarily on photographs by Raper and Quinlan, 1958.)

rounded body is a true spore or a microcyst (Fig. 8). This close relationship possibly reflects a phylogenetic link between the spores of the Acrasiales and the cysts of solitary amoebae.

Aggregation on the whole is typical of Acrasiales, although

some features are peculiar to *Acytostelium*. In particular, large networks of streams form which then fail to develop into sorocarps but eventually either break up into microcysts or "disintegrate," to use Shaffer's term. Smaller aggregation patterns, which gather in the usual fashion, rarely give rise to one sorocarp, but usually up to twenty-five or more. Each fruiting body begins in the form of a small papilla; and as culmination proceeds, aggregation continues for a considerable period (Fig. 10). As Raper and Quinlan point out, the overlap of aggregation and culmination, as well as the production of numerous sorocarps in one aggregation pattern, are features found to a lesser degree in other small forms, i.e. *D. lacteum* and *D. minutum*.

Each papilla rises into the air leaving a very thin hair of a stalk behind and the cell mass has the shape of a spindle. The cells within the mass are oriented almost entirely at right angles to the stalk, and at the anterior end there appear to be one or two "cap cells," as Raper calls them, which cover the tip completely, like keystones. Down the central axis of the cell mass there is a very fine hole, and if looked at in cross section the cells appear wedge-shaped, coming to a point at this central hole.

The hole, of course, is the site of deposition of the stalk which passes out posteriorly. The stalk is only 1 to 2 μ in diameter and its length is from about 750 to 1500 μ. Raper and Quinlan have shown that it is a tube of cellulose with a minute lumen.

With some material that was kindly sent to us by Raper, we have made periodic acid-Schiff preparations for non-starch polysaccharides and find that there are few signs of differentiation or specialization within the cells; they take up the stain uniformly. Ultimately, after the stalk has reached its full height all the cells become rounded spores; there is here no division of labor among the cells, but all the cells produce the stalk and then all the cells produce the sorus.

14. The phylogeny of the Acrasiales

In considering the phylogenetic position of *Acytostelium*, one of the first thoughts is whether or not this new form is an ancestor or a descendent of the other members of the Acrasiales. Raper and Quinlan (1958) have adopted the position that *Acytostelium* is an advance, while I have taken the opposite view (Bonner, 1957). Raper and Quinlan argue that since no cells are lost in the production of the stalk, this is a more efficient, more advanced form, although they admit that this advance has been made at the sacrifice of being able to achieve fruiting bodies of great length. It would seem to me that from the point of view of selection, the greater length, along with the increase in solidity of a cellular stalk, would have advantages that would outweigh the loss of a few cells, provided the remaining cells were sufficiently numerous to ensure the propagation of the species. As a matter of fact, because of the increase in size of the cellular stalk, the number of cells produced by one sorocarp of a larger slime mold is many times greater than that produced by the delicate *Acytostelium*.

Also it would seem that a division of labor among a cell population would represent an advance. In *Acytostelium* the same cell does both tasks, but in the other forms there is a differentiation and any one cell performs one task only.

Another point in support of the idea that *Acytostelium* is primitive is that the spores are spherical and closely resemble the microcysts. On the basis of this clue (and now I will build hypothesis upon hypothesis) one might suggest that separate amoebae capable of encystment acquired, by mutation and selection, two new characters: an ability to come together in aggregations, and the ability to secrete a supporting stalk.

This latter achievement may have occurred in the separate amoebae first, as it has in *Sappinia,* but this form, because of its large size and special nuclear characters is obviously not the precursor of *Acytostelium.* On the other hand, the ability to secrete stalk may have occurred only after the aggregation, for existing species do it as a communal project with one stalk for many spores (Fig. 11).

D. lacteum would seem to be suited for the next position in the family tree, its relation to *Acytostelium* being that they both possess round spores. But in this step upward there has been a great change. For increased rigidity and stability there is now a division of labor, and the anterior cells enter and become part of the cellulose tube they created, in that way producing a tapering structure of remarkable engineering design. Not only does it have the structural advantage of a tube (in common with *Acytostelium*), but also it has a taper as well as cross struts inside the tube, that is, the cellulose walls of the vacuolated stalk cells. Anticipating a future development, it should be added that the basal disc of *D. discoideum* is of further structural advantage, for it serves to exaggerate the taper at the base like the curved legs of the Eiffel tower or the spreading roots of a tree. It would be interesting to pursue this line of thought and see by experiment to what extent these delicate structures are a product of direct physical forces, following the lines of thought of D'Arcy Thompson (1917) and Harper (1926, et seq.), and to what extent they are genetically determined. The direct effect of mechanical forces on the shape of biological structures continues to be as absorbing a subject as it was under the stimulus of the neo-Lamarckians some years ago.

To return to *D. lacteum,* the division of labor of the cells also means that the spore cells do not waste their energy and their polysaccharide on stalk formation but save it for the period of hibernation and resistance.

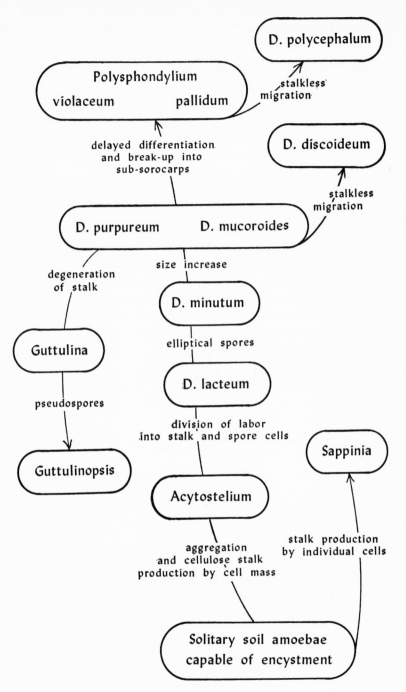

Fig. 11. An hypothetical phylogenetic tree of the Acrasiales.

The next change, presumably by some mutation, is the appearance of capsule-shaped spores, although it is hard to imagine what the selective advantage of this change in spore shape might be. In any event, a small form such as *D. minutum* would be the the result, for besides this feature there is little to distinguish *D. minutum* from *D. lacteum.*

D. minutum might be considered to be on the lower limit of the *mucoroides* complex, and one could postulate a selective pressure for an increase in size. This would have the advantage of producing a long stalk, in that way separating the site of vegetative growth from the site of sporulation by as great a distance as possible. The large *D. mucoroides* does have a prolonged period of migration, and the migrating mass shows effective tropisms towards light and heat. This would mean that the sorus now has a "better place in the sun," and that this has been achieved merely by increasing the size of the aggregate. The relation of *D. purpureum* is thought to be a simple one involving the pigmentation of the spore case.

Clearly, if very long stalks are produced in *D. mucoroides,* the number of cells left to form spores is correspondingly small. By having a stalkless migration period, as in *D. discoideum,* this obstacle is effectively overcome. That there is a direct transition between these two forms is suggested by the variants of *D. mucoroides,* which under certain conditions fail to produce stalks for short intervals. As mentioned above, *D. discoideum* has the added feature of a basal disc.[9]

If, now, a mutant of *D. mucoroides* delayed its differentiation and remained capable of breaking up into smaller groups at an advanced moment in its development, then under some conditions this increase in plasticity would be advantageous.

[9] Also Filosa (1958) has discovered a new mutant of *D. mucoroides* that has, under certain cultural conditions, a stalkless migrating pseudoplasmodium. However, by its irregular and somewhat abnormal appearance it can in no way be confused with *D. discoideum.* See page 121.

Furthermore, by breaking up into numerous small fruiting bodies spread over an area, dispersal of the spores might be enhanced. This, of course, is exactly what has happened in *Polysphondylium*. Again in this genus there are both purple and white spored forms which are believed to be closely related.

Finally, and this point has already been made, if *Polysphondylium*, which has the power of breaking up into subsorocarps at a late moment, should gain the power of the less wasteful, more efficient stalkless migration, then the result would be *D. polycephalum*. This step would in all respects be quite parallel to the change from *D. mucoroides* to *D. discoideum*.

We have failed to mention *Guttulina* and *Guttulinopsis* in this phylogenetic tree. No doubt Raper (1956b) is correct in supporting the contention of Olive (1902) and others that these are fixed types which do not result solely from the phenotypic effect of poor cultural conditions, as Cohen's (1953a) work might imply. From the work of Sussman and his group (Sussman and Sussman, 1953 et seq.) on mutants of *D. mucoroides* it seems reasonable to suggest that perhaps these forms are mutant forms, in which *Guttulinopsis* with its pseudospores shows the most extreme degeneration.

III. The Problem of Morphogenetic Movement

I N most animals and a few plants there are systematic movements of protoplasm that are responsible for shaping the organism during its development. The general importance in embryology of these so-called morphogenetic movements is very great, and therefore it is understandable that there should be such a deep interest in the controlling mechanism that guides the movements to produce constant shapes. Some progress has been made in the work with amphibian embryos, to a great extent due to the stimulus of the work of Holtfreter (1943 a, b; 1944), who emphasized the importance of adhesion between cells and the sticky materials that favor this adhesion, thereby causing the attached cells to act in a unified, coordinated fashion. The pioneer work of Harrison (1910) followed and extended in the important experiments of Weiss (1929, 1934, 1945) showed how moving or growing cells are sensitive to the ultrastructure and tensions of the environment, so that they may be coordinated in their morphogenetic movement by their immediate surroundings.

In contrast to this mechanical method of the control of formative cell movements, there has been a steady interest in the possibility that cells might orient within a gradient of a chemical substance by chemotaxis. This has turned out to be a difficult phenomenon to demonstrate in developing animals, although there are some cases where the evidence is excellent, such as the work of Twitty and Niu[1] on the factors affecting the distribution of pigment cells in amphibians.

[1] Reviewed in Twitty (1949). There is also good evidence for chemotaxis in the fertilization of numerous plants, and this subject is excellently reviewed by Rothschild (1956).

It would appear likely, then, that for organisms in general there are both mechanical and chemical factors concerned in the guiding of cell movements during development. If we now turn to the cellular slime molds, we find that here also there is evidence for both factors, and that they operate hand in hand. At least in the aggregation stage the analysis of the movement is a comparatively easy matter, for the material adapts itself readily to experiment. Following a discussion of aggregation we will pass on to the movements of migration and culmination, although unfortunately far less is known about these later stages.

1. The mechanism of aggregation

Both Olive (1902) and Potts (1902) made the independent suggestion that the aggregating cells are oriented to the central collection points by chemotaxis. Neither provided any evidence to support the hypothesis, although Olive did attempt, without success, to orient the amoebae by creating gradients with solutions of sugar and malic acid. This experiment was stimulated by the work of Pfeffer (see Rothschild, 1956), who had such striking success orienting the spermatozoa of bracken with these substances.

No further experimental work was attempted until 1942 when Runyon performed a notable experiment: if amoebae were put on two sides of a cellophane membrane, the aggregation streams on both sides were perfectly aligned, one above the other. In other words, the factor responsible for orientation could readily pass through the membrane. Runyon (1942) considered this further evidence for chemotaxis, but other possibilities remained, for a wide variety of agents other than small molecules could readily pass through cellophane. In view of this fact I attempted a number of experiments, examining the possibility that electric and other forces might be operating, but all save one provided negative results (Bonner, 1947). The successful experiment gave excellent evidence that chemotaxis was indeed involved. If the amoebae were allowed to aggregate on the bottom of a dish under a layer of water, and the water was moved gently over their surface (as though they were lying on the bottom of a brook), then the amoebae upstream of the center showed no orientation toward it and wandered about aimlessly, while the amoebae downstream were beautifully oriented toward the center and would move upstream from considerable distances to join it. This gave positive evidence of a free diffusing agent, and it was immediately evident that the agent was probably a chemical substance rather than heat, because it was known that the center of some species would not attract the amoebae of other species. This substance was given the generic name of "acrasin," which was intended to designate the chemotactic agent of any member of the Acrasiales.

The next step was to produce the substance *in vitro* and in this way have an absolute demonstration of its existence. I made numerous attempts to do this by taking agar on which a center presumably emitting acrasin had rested, and by taking freshly killed centers (killed in a wide variety of ways) and placing these non-living sources in among sensitive amoebae. In no case was there any evidence for chemotaxis. There were a number of reasons to suspect that either acrasin broke down rapidly or was volatile, and that since the agar blocks or dead centers were unable to produce new acrasin, what was there originally was soon lost and the gradient obliterated. Of course, even if there were acrasin present and it had a uniform distribution, there would be no chemotaxis, for the orientation of cells by a diffusing chemical can only be achieved if the chemical is in a gradient; there must be more molecules bombarding one end of the cells than the other, thus providing information about direction to the amoeba. Experiments were devised to see if aggregation could occur across a moist air barrier rather than the usual aqueous barrier, but there was no evidence for a volatile chemotactic agent from these experiments.

In 1950 Pfützner-Eckert, working in the laboratory of A. Kühn, reported that she was able to obtain orientation toward agar blocks which had been in contact with centers of *D. mucoroides* and then placed among sensitive amoebae. This is quite contrary to my experiments on *D. discoideum*, and Shaffer (1956b) reports that he was unable to repeat these experiments with *D. mucoroides*. The explanation of this enigma is unknown and it is hoped that it will someday be solved. Shaffer also reports many other types of unsuccessful experiments using agar blocks in different ways and killing active acrasin-secreting sources in a variety of manners.

In order to circumvent the possibility that in such experiments the acrasin gradient disappears, Shaffer (1953, 1956b) devised an ingenious experiment which provided the first unequivocal demonstration of the chemical nature of the aggregation phenomenon. Sensitive amoebae are sandwiched between a glass slide and a minute block of agar (2 to 3 mm. square). This is placed within a moist chamber, and alongside on the glass slide are put a number of cell masses actively producing acrasin. A small drop of water is added beside each one of these acrasin sources. With a fine pipette or a glass rod a cell-free drop[2] is removed from the vicinity of one of the sources and placed on the side of the agar block so that a meniscus is formed. This same operation is repeated at short intervals, each time taking the drop from a fresh source. The amoebae in the glass-agar sandwich will, in five to ten minutes, show an orientation to the nearest edge of the block, and then proceed to move toward it.

[2] This was checked by passing the drop through a millipore filter before using it (Shaffer, 1956b).

Consider now the logic of this experiment. The amoebae are wedged by an agar block so there can be no convection, as would be the case with amoebae merely placed under water. The meniscus at the edge provides a firm site where the acrasin source remains fixed. The gradient is maintained by the repeated additions of fresh acrasin-water, for if the acrasin is destroyed and if diffusion tends to rapidly obliterate an original gradient, this will be counteracted by supplying the material at constant intervals over a period. It should be added that Shaffer has tried a variety of controls using plain water and differently shaped blocks and adding the acrasin-water in different ways; these have all supported the interpretation that this is a valid and clear-cut *in vitro* demonstration of acrasin.

The next step was to examine its stability. By holding the acrasin-water in a pipette for various time intervals before applying it to the meniscus, Shaffer showed that the acrasin, in a matter of a few minutes, lost its potency and no longer was capable of orienting the amoebae. With fresh acrasin-water positive results were obtained if the intervals between application at the meniscus varied between ten seconds and two minutes. If, however, the acrasin water was stored five minutes before application, it had either a weak effect or none at all, even if it was reapplied at short intervals. On the other hand, when these pipettes full of acrasin water were quickly frozen with dry ice, they could be stored for long periods, and if quickly warmed up and used at short intervals, they retained their original activity. Clearly, then, acrasin was for some reason unstable at room temperature, but in a frozen condition it retained its full potency.

In further analyzing the problem of its stability, Shaffer (1956a, b) found that if he allowed the aggregation streams or acrasin sources to lie on one side of a dializing membrane, and if he then collected acrasin-water from the opposite side, the acrasin was stable for long periods at room temperature. The obvious inference is that the acrasin is normally destroyed by some substance of large molecular weight, presumably a protein enzyme. He also has shown that if cold methanol was poured over the cultures in petri dishes and then vacuum-dried in the cold, and eventually the residue brought into aqueous solution, this preparation was both active and stable. It is hoped that this now brings us to the threshold of some understanding of the chemistry of acrasin.

Following this work on stabilization Sussman, Lee, and Kerr (1956) found a totally different method of obtaining stable acrasin. They immersed cultures in cold dilute HCl at pH 3.5, the resulting solution was shown to be stable and active, using Shaffer's test. By fractionation methods they were able to separate the acrasin into two components, both of which were necessary in a specific ratio for optimum activity.[3] Their results strongly support the notion that acrasin is degraded enzymatically.

There are a number of reasons, as Shaffer (1956b, 1957a) emphasizes, why the destruction of acrasin might be of great importance in the aggregation process. This would effectively increase the relative gradient of acrasin, as well as lower its total concentration. The lowering of the total concentration is especially important where the amount of liquid medium surrounding the aggregate is small, such as aggregation taking place on a thin film of moisture on the surface of a glass

[3] In a recent abstract R. R. Sussman, M. Sussman, and F. Lee Fu (1958) further report the isolation of a third fraction, again emphasizing the importance of the ratios for activity. Also, B. E. Wright (1958) has presented an interesting abstract in which she states that the urine of a pregnant woman is highly active in the Shaffer test. Apparently this is due to the steroids in the urine, for estradiol, progesterone, testosterone, and a number of other steroids are active (while a group of related compounds are not). It will be interesting to see if the naturally occurring acrasins are steroids of this type, or whether these compounds act in a secondary fashion in the way they appear to be doing in the induction studies on amphibians.

slide. For high concentrations of acrasin in such small quantities of water would soon produce a large "background noise," making the problem of detecting a gradient most difficult.

In a series of papers Shaffer (1956b, 1957a, b, c, 1958) has elaborated his views on the overall mechanism of aggregation. One of his principle points is that aggregation is not the simple and therefore tempting picture of one large acrasin gradient containing a mass of amoebae streaming to the point of highest concentration. Not only must the chemotaxis mechanism be set down in quite different terms, but also, along with the chemotaxis there are mechanical factors of considerable importance that are operating in conjunction with the chemical mechanism. Certain aspects of this position have been appreciated by earlier authors, but no one has made so many detailed observations and been able to take so comprehensive a view.

One of the most bewildering facets of aggregation is the tremendous variation in the normal patterns and in the response to experimental treatment. By comparing the details of four different species (*D. discoideum, D. mucoroides, D. purpureum* and *P. violaceum*) Shaffer finds that the variation is not species specific, but rather that the whole gamut of variation can occur within any one species. Furthermore, the environmental conditions have remarkably little importance in promoting this, but rather, the variability in the course of aggregation seems to be an innate part of the behavior of these simple organisms. Without entering here into the details of the variation, they can, with considerable success, be attributed to four states of the individual cells. The cells may be constantly shifting back and forth from one state to another before the final progressive, integrative forces take over to produce a completed pseudoplasmodium.

The first state is characteristic of the unaggregated cells

that can neither produce acrasin nor respond to it. In the second they can produce and react to acrasin, but they are separate and as yet unaggregated. In the third they react, they emit acrasin, and they have become mutually sticky so the cells adhere one to another to form streams. Finally in the fourth the properties are the same as in the third state except that the cells have entered the center and become more nearly rounded and stationary. They continue to show stickiness and acrasin emission (Plates V, VI, VII).

The one step in this chain that is particularly important is that from the second to the third state. If separate sensitive amoebae are bathed by acrasin from a nearby source, they will become sticky and produce acrasin of their own. The acrasin itself initiates these reactions. It might be thought that this stage of integration is only reached when an amoeba enters a stream, but the action can occur at a distance. To ascertain this point Shaffer kept moving a center away from some separate amoebae that were approaching it, and finally the separate amoebae clumped together into a compact, sticky, acrasin-secreting stream that had no connection with the constantly dislodged center. Shaffer sums up this observation by stating that it is acrasin itself that induces integration among the amoebae. The word "induction" is used here advisedly, for acrasin, besides operating in the chemotaxis, actively transforms the cells into a new state, one in which there has been a change in the surface properties of the cells so that they will now adhere to one another.

It had been known before that once the cells do adhere, their individual movements affect one another. This was shown, for instance, in some experiments already cited, when a section of an aggregating stream was cut out, turned 180°, and reattached to the stump that was entering into the center (Bonner, 1950). The reversed piece was then literally pulled into the center as though it were a piece of treacle. The cells in the intact stump of the stream were actively moving toward the center, and exerted a pull-tension on the reversed segment of stream, causing the cells within that segment to follow the tension. This is consistent with views of Weiss (1929, 1934, 1945) that cells are affected by mechanical forces in their immediate environment, all of which means that besides chemotaxis, an important factor in orienting the cells to a common center is the mechanical one of pull tensions. This is possible because the cells have become sticky and adhere to one another—a property which arises as the result of the action of acrasin on the cells. Therefore, even though aggregation must be thought of in terms of both chemotaxis and mechanical factors, acrasin is involved in both aspects, and is, in this sense, the overseeing, controlling agent in aggregation.

But one important fact has been left unexplained. How do the cells within a stream become oriented so that they all move towards the center? This brings us again to the intriguing problem of polarity, and in a stream there would seem to be a rather rigid polarity of movement. All the cells are going the same way and they appear to mutually pull at one another so that there can be no strays, no contrary individuals; since pull-tensions are most effective in orienting the cells, they will all go the way the majority goes.

That the direction of movement within a stream is mechanical is supported by a revealing set of experiments of Shaffer. He tested the acrasin emission of different portions of streams and centers by placing the streams and the centers in competition for some random amoebae (Bonner, 1949). In this way he showed that the streams emitted just as much acrasin as the centers, and there was no evidence at all for an overall gradient of acrasin in the whole aggregate (Plate VIII). As he points out, it is impossible, at the moment, to detect what small internal (and perhaps ephemeral) gradients there might be within the mass, but the evidence suggests that the cells in the stream work on a mechanical follow-the-leader principle, and that the direction must be imparted to them in the beginning. A final bit of evidence to support this concept is the formation of rings (Arndt, 1937; Raper, 1941; Bonner, 1950; Shaffer, 1957c). These frequently occur at the center of an aggregation pattern, and there is no apex, but a circle of cells adhering to one another, and continuously moving around.

This still leaves us with the problem of the original orientation before the streams are formed; the orientation that gives the cells of streams their first instructions as to direction. It is the common presumption that at the onset of aggregation, certain cells begin to secrete acrasin sooner than others. As Shaffer has shown, the entering of the acrasin-secreting stage may not be a permanent one, but there may be a reversion to the non-secreting stage. Ultimately, however, in this backing and filling, a stable center is formed, and it emits acrasin. The isolated amoebae that surrounds it will now, for a short period, be bathed in a gradient of acrasin, and will accordingly orient towards the center. The reason that the period will be short is twofold: the acrasin will be rapidly inactivated, and it will stimulate these outlying cells to secrete acrasin of their own. The gradient, therefore, would soon be obliterated and be replaced by a more uniform distribution of acrasin. It is unlikely, however, that the entire future orientation of a pattern could be controlled by this single initial gradient of acrasin, even if we assume that it could be relayed outward to more distant amoebae by the intermediate ones that have begun to emit acrasin after having been stimulated by the center.

Since one direction signal is probably not enough to account for the whole subsequent aggregation, Shaffer has suggested an ingenious hypothetical explanation which assumes a series of such directional impulses, one following the next. The center, which now is the pacemaker, emits some acrasin, and a gradient is set up in its immediate vicinity. The adjacent amoebae are oriented and eventually stimulated to produce acrasin. The orientation, however, occurs first, before the first surge of acrasin has been largely inactivated, and before these secondary amoebae produce a surge of acrasin of their own. This new surge produces a new gradient which now spreads to the amoebae beyond it and produces similar orientation and subsequent stimulation. Since the gradient is first in a position to orient the cells correctly toward the center, the fact that subsequently there is either no gradient or a reverse gradient, is insufficient, according to the hypothesis, to override the effect of the first gradient which acted upon the cell in a receptive period before it became "fatigued" and before it secreted its own acrasin. If the center emits acrasin rhythmically, then with each new impulse the peripheral amoebae will receive a new directional message; in fact by repeating the message, the center retains its key position as a pacemaker.

These impulses could be, as Shaffer points out, the rhythmic waves of fast inward motion revealed by the time lapse motion pictures. These waves start in the center and radiate outward; they are a wave of fast inward motion of the individual amoebae.

Once the amoebae are oriented towards a common point, they will coalesce into streams, for acrasin not only induces the cells to produce their own acrasin, but induces stickiness as well. The streams themselves actively produce acrasin, and therefore they can in turn attract separate amoebae in just the way a center is capable of doing. It is possible to see the rhythmic waves pass down a stream, and therefore the ability to relay the acrasin emission is presumably possible within a stream as well as between separate amoebae. It is for this reason that the importance of acrasin activity in orienting the amoebae within a stream is in some doubt, although the fact that mechanical factors also play a significant role remains an excellent possibility.

The relay hypothesis of Shaffer has the merit of explaining two facts which would seem to be inconsistent. The first is that chemotaxis unquestionably occurs, and the second is that Shaffer was often unable to demonstrate any difference in the amount of acrasin secreted by centers and different parts of streams. These facts are satisfied by the hypothesis that there is no overall gradient, but a relay system of small ephemeral gradients. A further advantage of the idea is that it can explain the large aggregation expanses of oriented amoebae that occur before the final aggregation patterns in some species. It is a method that can operate at a great distance, provided there are scattered intermediate cells to carry the message outward. We now have a far more realistic and sophisticated view of the aggregation mechanism than was possible a few years ago. There is, however, still room for future experiment and observation, for there remain many assumptions which must be pushed to the level of fact.

There is also another interesting aspect that needs an explanation: what controls the size of an aggregate? It is an old observation that the average size of aggregates or the average size of the fruiting bodies is directly related to the density of the vegetative amoebae prior to aggregation. The matter has been examined in detail by Sussman and his group (reviewed by Sussman, 1956b), who finds that each species (and different mutant variants) has a characteristic cell density at which fruiting occurs most efficiently, at least in the sense that there are the greatest number of fruiting bodies per unit area. For example, in *D. discoideum* if the vegetative cells are at a density of 200 cells per mm^2, then the number of fruiting bodies per mm^2 will be at a maximum, and higher or lower cell densities will produce fewer fruiting bodies

(Sussman and Noël, 1952). Unfortunately the information is incomplete on the size of the fruiting bodies, for the mean size of the fruiting bodies at the optimum density is about 2200 cells per sorocarp, but in greater cell densities all that is known is that the fruiting bodies are larger.[4] Therefore this optimum of Sussman and Noël represents an optimum for the largest number of small fruiting bodies rather than the largest fruiting bodies. It has the merit of being a stable quantity that can be measured with accuracy, and in this way comparisons can be made between species and strains. For example, the optimum density for large numbers of small fruiting bodies in *D. purpureum* is 100 cells/mm² (in contrast to the 200 cells/mm² of *D. discoideum*), and it is 350 cells/mm² for a "bushy" mutant of *D. discoideum*. Another mutant of *D. discoideum* ("fruity") that was discovered by Sussman (1955a) has characteristically very small fruiting bodies. The optimal density for the largest number of small fruiting bodies was again 200 cells/mm², but its unique feature was that at this optimal density the fruiting bodies averaged merely 24 cells (in contrast to 2200 cells of the normal *D. discoideum*).

These results of Sussman clearly indicate that there is a marked control of the size of aggregation, and that this depends to some extent on the density of the original amoeba population, and to a large extent on the genetic constitution of the strain used. The question now is: how do cell density and these unknown genetic or intrinsic factors operate? For some time Sussman himself championed the idea that there were a certain number of specific cells that were different or special in some fixed way, and he underscored this hypothesis by calling them "initiator cells." It was Sussman (1956a, b)

[4] This was determined in a preliminary experiment I did some years ago (1946), in which the largest sorocarps were produced at cell densities of 600 to 1000 amoebae/mm.²

himself, however, who ruled out the possibility of a genetically distinct cell type. If there was to be a fixed proportion of
such initiator cells (1 in 2200 in the case of *D. discoideum*),
then this must have arisen as a result of the division of the
cells, so that by division in a vegetative population 1 in 2200
cells would have this special character. But he was able to
show that amoebae taken from any phase of the growth cycle,
including newly germinated spores, gave fruiting bodies of
2200 cells at a cell density of 200 cells/mm^2. Therefore, this
capacity is not the special province on one cell in 2200, but
something that can arise in any group of cells of sufficient
size and density; it is possible, for instance, that a certain
per cent of the cells arrive at the aggregative condition sooner
than the others, or that the cells show a range of variation of
some other character. Also, Sussman indicates that a great
deal of the effect possibly lies in the extent to which the cells
respond to the aggregation forces, as well as the role of environmental factors. For instance, certain chemical substances
such as histidine will affect the number of centers at a particular cell density (Bradley, Sussman, and Ennis, 1956), as
will washings of extracts of various strains on a test strain
(Sussman, 1955a; Ennis and Sussman, 1958). The problem
then narrows down to physiological differences among cells,
and these differences are influenced by many factors.[5]

But we still are without an explanation of the factors af-

[5] See Shaffer (1958) for a discussion of center initiation. Recently
Ennis and Sussman (1958b) claim that they can visually identify "initiator
cells." However, the matter is in need of further investigation because their
criteria for identification are subjective and their evidence that the cells
are causally connected with center formation is indirect. The key difficulty
with the notion is that there is as yet no firm evidence that the aggregation
cells vary in a discontinuous manner. The fact that they do vary is clear,
and it is most reasonable to assume that cells at one end of the spectrum
of variants will more likely be associated with the initiation of the centers
than the other cells. But the exact details of the process of initiation are
still wanting. (Also see Jaffe (1958) for a critical discussion of this
matter.)

fecting size of fruiting bodies. Sussman has shown that size can be, under constant conditions, a remarkably consistent phenomenon, and there is some general notion that the magnitude of the stimulus (presumably acrasin production) and the sensitivity of the response are involved. In any event, the solution will have to take into consideration more complex matters such as pulsations and stickiness; there is still a need for more work and thought on this problem.

2. The mechanism of the migration movement

Far less is known about the mechanism of movement during migration than is known for the aggregation stage. This is due largely to the fact that during migration the cells are bunched together, and it is more difficult to observe them individually. Inevitably there has been considerable speculation as to mechanism, and I shall attempt here to summarize both the facts and the hypotheses. Most of the work on migration has been performed on *D. discoideum*, but there is no reason to believe that the problems are not the same for those species that manufacture stalk during migration. Since a discussion of the movement during culmination will follow, the special problem of the movement of the cells actively forming a stalk will be considered in that section.

The most obvious kind of factual information that can be gathered for migration is on the speed of movement of the mass. This has been done in some detail for *D. discoideum*, and it was found that the larger the migrating pseudoplasmodium, the faster it moved (Bonner, Koontz, and Paton, 1953). It was even possible to follow individual pseudoplasmodia that became smaller with continued migration, and the rate of movement dropped correspondingly. At 20°C the range of rates extended from 0.3 to 2.0 mm per hour.[6]

[6] Raper (1956b) finds the rate of the migrating pseudoplasmodium of

From this we argued that all the cells are contributing to the movement and there is no surface layer of active cells that transports the remainder as an inert mass. The argument was suggested by the work of Tyler (1942) who made a similar proposition for the rates of development of whole and half sea urchin embryos. The point is that, according to the principle of similitude, bodies of similar shape will have an increase in the ratio of volume to surface area as the size increases. If in the migrating cell masses the surface provides friction, and the propelling mass is a function of the volume, then in larger masses the speed will be greater, for the frictional resistance will be small relative to the propelling mass of amoebae. This hypothesis assumes that the power of movement per unit mass of cells is constant for different size pseudoplasmodia, and Gregg (1950) gives support to this assumption by showing that the oxygen utilization per unit nitrogen of tissue is the same for small and large cell masses.

Before this hypothesis can be properly evaluated it is necessary to record a few observations. First of all, there is a great deal of evidence to suggest that the traction occurs between the slime sheath and the amoebae, rather than between the sheath and the environment. The sheath is stationary and is laid out as a carpet upon which the amoebae may tread. Not only can this be shown by placing markers on the sheath which do not move as the cell mass pulls out from under them, but also the whole migrating mass will move at the same rate, whether it is touching the substratum over most of its surface or whether it is partially pointed up into the air. This latter condition may be so exaggerated that merely the hind end of the slug is touching the substratum, a condition especially striking in the case of the long string-like pseudoplasmodia of *D. polycephalum*. Also, both *D. dis-*

D. polycephalum about 0.5 mm/hour, which is consistent with *D. discoideum*, especially as *D. polycephalum* is so thin.

coideum and *D. polycephalum* will migrate across the hyphae of some common mold, never touching the agar surface for great distances, but merely touching one hypha after another as though they were passing through the branches of some minute tree.

If the migrating slug is allowed to crawl onto a coverslip, and the coverslip is then inverted in a small moist chamber, it is possible to observe the cells with high powers of the microscope for some depth. Such observations could be profitably extended and a detailed analysis made, yet a short glance will show that the cells are all actively pseudopodial and that they do not move at exactly the same rate; their relative positions will vary to some extent over the course of a few minutes. The significance of this latter point will be discussed shortly, but for the present the fact that the cells are actively moving by amoeboid motion is clear.

It is possible now to compare the speed of movement of migrating masses and individual amoebae, and it is found that they are of the same order of magnitude. This was shown in an old unpublished experiment where some isolated amoebae were alongside a migrating pseudoplasmodium of *D. discoideum* and the amoebae, apparently oriented by the acrasin of the slug, kept pace with it: the speeds of the two were the same. This fact has also been ascertained by measuring the speed of amoebae during aggregation. Since movement during the vegetative stage is such a random affair, it is difficult to obtain any meaningful estimate of rate.

There are, then, three main points of information upon which we may build a hypothetical view of the mechanism of movement: 1) the slime sheath is stationary, 2) all the cells within the mass are actively moving, and 3) the cells inside the mass move at approximately the same rate as cells outside the mass. This suggests that movement within the migrating mass is basically no different from that of an aggregation stream. All the cells are moving forward, but they are in so thick a mass as a migration slug, that the question soon arises as to how the cells in the interior of the mass obtain traction. The case is clear enough for those at the edge, because they are adjacent to the slime sheath, but does the sheath material extend inward like a net to give traction to all the cells? Unfortunately we do not know the answer to this question, for the sheath is so extremely thin that it is impossible to follow it internally, and whether all the cells or just the external ones secrete it cannot be determined as yet. However, an internal slime net may not be necessary to explain how traction is provided for the internal amoebae. When amoebae move, much of their external wall expanse is rigid, and the central channel of protoplasm which pours out to the tip is relatively fluid. If the walls are rigid (at least for short periods of time) and the cells are sticky and adhere to one another, then they will provide one another with temporary traction. Each amoeba lays down its own carpet in the form of its solid gel wall; the gel walls in turn stick to one another and ultimately to the slime sheath. It is true that these adhering walls are constantly torn down and built anew, but at any one instant there is a firm framework or skeleton of gel wall that, like a three dimensional net, penetrates the whole migrating cell mass.

It was mentioned that the cells do not all travel at the same rate, and this matter may now be examined in more detail. When Raper (1940b) made his original grafts of white and red fractions of migrating pseudoplasmodia (stained by growing the cells on the red bacterium *Serratia marcescens*), he showed that the division line stays constant for a number of hours. Since then, we have found two exceptions to this general rule.

The first is at the end of aggregation. Recently we have made similar grafts during the aggregation stage; that is, a colorless aggregation center is placed in front of an aggregating stream in which the amoebae have been vitally stained with Nile blue sulphate (Bonner and Adams, 1958). Theoretically this should produce a migrating slug in which the anterior half is colorless and the posterior half blue (or vice versa, if a blue center was grafted onto colorless amoebae), for such would be the case if the graft had been made during the migration stage. The fact is, however, that the slug will be uniformly blue, indicating that at the end of aggregation there is a critical period in which there is a violent cell redistribution. There is no known counterpart at a latter stage; it is only at the end of aggregation that one has this great mixing of the cells within the mass.

The second exception to the notion that during migration the cells keep a fixed position is the observation that the division line does not remain completely sharp, but there are a few cells which wander past it (Bonner, 1952, 1957). If a colorless tip is grafted onto a hind end stained with Nile blue sulphate, individual blue cells can be seen wandering forward in the colorless tip. If the reverse graft is made, the individual blue cells can be seen to fall backward, indicating that throughout migration there are a few cells that are especially fast and are moving forward, and a few that are especially slow that lag behind. It is even possible to measure the speed of these cells, and in a large pseudoplasmodium it takes approximately six hours for a fast cell to pass from the mid-region of a migrating sausage to the tip.

These vital stain experiments have been done entirely on *D. discoideum*, but there is evidence for at least the slow-moving cells in *D. mucoroides* (Bonner, 1957). These accumulate in the posterior end and take on the staining properties of the pre-stalk cells; earlier in this book I have referred to them as the rear-guard cells. In a particular strain of *D. mucoroides* it is possible to measure the increase in the size of the rear-guard zone as migration proceeded. For a long period there was a slow accumulation of cells in this posterior zone, but after 5 cm. of migration the rate suddenly rose sharply. In *D. discoideum*, where the rear-guard cells apparently form the basal disc, there is no such accumulation, and the zone stays approximately the same size. As mentioned before, the reason for this is that the cells are constantly left behind and lost in the slime track. Therefore the size of the basal disc is the same for those individuals that have migrated hardly at all and those that have migrated great distances.

The fact that all the cells do not have the same potential of movement was also ascertained by another experiment (Bonner, 1952). If some vitally stained cells from the anterior end of *D. discoideum* were grafted onto the posterior end of a colorless migrating slug, then in a matter of two or three hours this colored segment has moved up to the anterior position corresponding to its original location. While moving, the colored mass remained discrete, and as the whole sausage migrated, the colored cells moved faster in a sharp band which finally reached the forward position. If a group of colored posterior cells were transplanted into the anterior end of a sausage, they would slowly lag and eventually assume a posterior position. If anterior pieces were placed in anterior positions and posterior pieces in posterior positions, their location remained fixed even after prolonged migration.

Another instance of a change in the relative positions of the groups of cells is a recent experiment in which the center of *D. discoideum* is placed among the aggregating streams of a particular strain of *D. mucoroides* (Bonner and Adams, 1958). Presumably this should produce a migrating mass with the anterior end *D. discoideum* and the posterior end *D. mucoroides*, but apparenlty the *D. mucoroides* cells are faster than the *D. discoideum*, for they pass through the latter and take over the anterior position. If the reverse graph is made, the anteriorly placed *D. mucoroides* remain in position and there is no change.

The above reversal in position may well take place during the period of violent cell redistribution at the end of aggregation. This, however, cannot be the case when the vital dye grafts are made during the migration stage. It may be that there is in any population of cells a range of cell velocities. At the end of aggregation these cells soon sort themselves out with the relatively fast ones in front and the relatively slow ones behind. As migration proceeds, a few stragglers continue to shift their positions, and some cells may even change into either fast or slow cells and then shift their position. The implications of these differences in rate of movement, as far as differentiation is concerned, will be discussed in the next chapter, but here, in a consideration of the mechanism of migration movement, they underline the fact that each amoeba is relatively independent in its movement, and that to some extent the whole migrating sausage is a mass of such independent cells bound by their stickiness and the slime sheath.

There is, however, clearly, some organized coordination of the migrating cells over and above being stuck together— a matter of considerable importance that deserves attention. Unfortunately, however, it is easier to show evidence for such coordination than to provide explanations of mechanism.

The most obvious evidence of coordination is the fact that the cells move in the same direction. This is a property that the migrating mass shares with the aggregation stream, and in both there is the likely possibility that follow-the-leader pull-tensions play a significant role. There is, it must be admitted, one significant difference between the two: in aggregation the cells are all lined up with their long axes in the direction of motion, while during migration the cells are far more rounded, and often, in the thinner anterior portion, they line up with their long axes at right angles to the direction of movement. The reason for this perplexing orientation is not known, although it is possible to suggest a hypothetical explanation. If one assumes that the forward movement of the cell mass depends upon each cell pushing out slime sheath material (which subsequently congeals) at its posterior end, then, at least in the posterior region, there is an obvious polarized deposition of slime which serves as a fixed support for the forward thrust. In the anterior region it can be seen in stained sections that the transversely oriented, spindle-shaped cells are attached to the surface sheath, and one is reminded of Holtfreter's (1943 a, b; 1944) description of the "bottle cells" attached to the surface coat in the embryos of amphibians. These cells, therefore, appear to be simultaneously secreting slime at one end and for some reason reaching into the interior at the other end. Their reaching inward might possibly be caused by chemotaxis and an internal gradient, or it may simply be that the slime sheath ends of the cells have better traction and therefore move forward more rapidly, with the result that the inner portions lag and become transversely oriented. In other words, the orientation would be the result of a differential rate of movement between the inside and the outside layers (Fig. 12).[7]

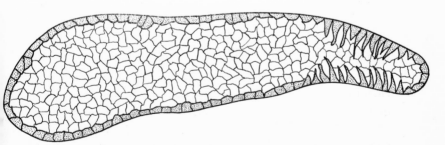

Fig. 12. A semi-diagrammatic view of a section of a migrating pseudoplasmodium of *D. discoideum* showing the typical transverse orientation of the cells in the narrow anterior portion.

[7] I am indebted to Prof C. H. Waddington for this suggestion.

Another important indication of coordination of the cells within the mass are the delicate tropisms of the whole mass: the fact that the mass will move towards light and towards warmer regions. In this case there is a sharp difference between the activities of the aggregating stream and a migrating mass. During aggregation it is impossible to induce one or a group of amoebae in a severed stream to show any orientation with respect to light and heat.

On the other hand, the migrating mass does show such tropisms, and these were first studied in detail by Raper (1940a, b, 1941b). He worked primarily with *D. discoideum*, although the phenomenon was shown to be present in *D. mucoroides* and *P. violaceum* as well. The matter was later reinvestigated quantitatively in our laboratory, and we found that the migrating pseudoplasmodia of *D. discoideum* were remarkably sensitive to heat gradients (Bonner, Clarke, Neely, and Slifkin, 1950). In a gradient of 0.05°C/cm. they could readily orient towards a warmer region. This means that in small pseudoplasmodia the temperature difference between the two sides would be of the order or magnitude of 0.0005°C. Also, a study was made of the spectral limits of the effect of light, but with the intensities used, no limit was found. From this it was suggested that the light acted by being absorbed more on one side of the pseudoplasmodium than the other, and this difference of absorption produced enough difference in heat to account for the turning.

This latter conclusion—that there is no discrete photochemical event—is probably incorrect, considering the subsequent studies of Gamble (1953). By using light sources of low intensity, such as luminescent bacteria and phosphorescent paint, and by carefully preventing any positive temperature gradient in the culture, he was able to show that the intensity of illumination necessary to produce orientation is far too low to be accounted for on the basis of heat absorption. This conclusion means that there is probably both a heat-sensitive and a light-sensitive mechanism, and we can only marvel at the extreme sensitivity in both cases.

There are reports in the literature of other tropisms, but their existence is still uncertain and more experiments are needed. Raper (1939, 1940b) has suggested that they show a chemotaxis and will move from an alkaline to an acid region, but despite repeated attempts we have not been able to confirm this. Potts (1902) suggested that in *D. mucoroides* the mass will migrate towards drier regions, and recently we have made a series of attempts to duplicate this result. It is possible that there is a slight effect, as some of our experiments show, but at best it is a vague and uncertain response.[8]

In trying to imagine how light and heat orient the migrating pseudoplasmodium, one cannot help but wonder if in some way acrasin might be involved. There is no evidence at all to support this notion; in fact, the whole fanciful suggestion comes entirely from wishful envy of the plant physiologist, who can so neatly explain many facets of photo- and geotropism on the basis of the distribution of auxin. If, in some way, light and heat would cause an increase in the production of acrasin on one side of the sausage, and if acrasin were still effective in orienting the direction of movement of the migrating amoebae, then there might be an acrasin-controlled mechanism of tropisms. There are, unfortunately, too many "ifs" in this thought. It is true that the tip of the sausage appears to be the site of the response mechanism to these external agents, but even this conclusion must be approached with caution, for after all, the tip is the only part that is capable of choosing a direction; all the other parts of the sausage are encased in the slime sheath and can only follow slavishly.

[8] Negative hydrotaxis was suggested by von Schuckmann (1925) and Harper (1926) to be the cause of aggregation, but, of course, this idea is of historical interest only.

There is, however, excellent evidence that the migrating body produces acrasin, as I have shown for *D. discoideum* (Bonner, 1949) and Pfützner-Eckert (1950) has shown for *D. mucoroides*. Furthermore, it was possible to demonstrate that in *D. discoideum* the tip produces more acrasin than the rest of the slug. This was done in two ways: 1) by cutting the tip off and allowing it to compete with the remaining larger portion for a field of randomly distributed, sensitive amoebae, and 2) by noting the direction at which incoming cells would approach an intact migrating mass. In the first method the small tip showed a greater influence over the surrounding amoebae than all the remaining portion, and in the second method the amoebae approaching the flank of a slug did so at an oblique angle, pointing to some extent toward the anterior region.

Another interesting fact is the observation of Shaffer (1953, 1957a) that at the migration stage *P. violaceum* would appear to be producing two acrasins, one which attracts the amoebae of *Polysphondylium* and one which attracts the amoebae of *Dictyostelium*, while at an earlier stage it only produces the *Polysphondylium* acrasin. Shaffer cautions that his results might have other possible interpretations, but that this is the most likely one. Assuming it is the case, it might argue for the *Dictyostelium* acrasin being in some way concerned in those processes that occur solely in the migration stage for both species. This is, of course, again hopelessly speculative. All we can say with any confidence in this whole situation is that acrasin is present in the migration stage, and, this being the case, it may possibly be important in some way in the morphogenetic processes.

The final aspect of migration that deserves attention is the problem of its duration. What external factors favor the continuation of migration, and what factors favor the onset of culmination and the final differentiation? The first clue to the problem came from a series of experiments in which we demonstrated that the concentration of solutes in the agar, all other factors being equal, had a profound effect on migration in *D. discoideum* (Slifkin and Bonner, 1952). The higher the concentration of solutes, the shorter the length of migration.[9] On plain, non-nutrient, two per cent agar the migration averaged ten days, with one extreme case of migration for twenty days. In some instances, if the slug was small from the beginning, it would just migrate until it disappeared, presumably because of the loss of cells in the slime track and the consuming of its energy reserves in these optimal conditions for migration.

The same technique has more recently been used with *D. mucoroides* with a similar result, but because *D. mucoroides* produces a continuous stalk during migration, it has certain advantages for such a study (Bonner and Shaw, 1957). In fact, it was possible to show that very small changes in humidity had a profound effect on migration; the slightest decrease would cause migration to stop and spore differentiation to commence. If a migrating mass is lifted off the surface of the agar there is apparently a sufficient difference between the relative humidity near the surface of the agar and that a few millimeters away to stimulate the beginning of the final differentiation. This was first discovered quite by accident in an experiment in which a number of migrating pseudoplasmodia of *D. mucoroides* were on a non-nutrient agar, moving toward a small light source. Through some error, one of the culture dishes was placed upside down, and as the stalk produced by the cell masses lengthened, the weight of the masses became excessive, causing them to swing down as though they were hanging from an agar ceiling. Almost

[9] Electrolytes were found to be slightly more effective than non-electrolytes at equivalent molar concentrations. There still is no satisfactory explanation of this difference.

as soon as they had become detached from the agar surface they ceased migration. This could be repeated in right-side-up culture dishes by raising the light source at an angle above the petri dish. Now, in order to migrate toward the light they had to rise upward at an angle of about 30°. Of course they kept falling back onto the agar when their stalks became too long, but on the average, culture dishes that were at such an angle from the light source fruited much sooner than plates which were on the same plane with the light. The point was checked in other ways, especially using solutions of sulphuric acid which lowered the relative humidity of the atmosphere over them, and all the results confirmed the view that relative humidity was of extreme importance.

This view conforms with the opinion of Raper (1940b), who showed that by lifting the cover off of the culture dishes for short periods it was possible to induce *D. discoideum* migrating pseudoplasmodia to enter into the culmination phase. Also, it should be mentioned that Potts (1902) was keenly aware of the importance of relative humidity, although he considered it to play a role in transpiration. He believed that in *D. mucoroides* stalk formation was promoted by a slight decrease in relative humidity so that transpiration could operate and that saturated conditions inhibited fruiting. We now know that his experiments under saturated conditions are more likely interpreted in terms of lack of oxygen or the accumulation of toxic substances such as ammonia (Cohen, 1953a). Potts himself showed that if they were grown in a sealed container with air bubbled through a water trap over the culture, good development resulted, but he was so convinced of his transpiration hypothesis that he sought other explanations for this experiment.

Our results with relative humidity on *D. mucoroides* led us to suggest that the reason that increasing the solute concentration reduced the extent of migration was because it effectively lowered the humidity at the surface of the agar. Since the organisms give every evidence of being extremely sensitive to desiccation, there is no reason why the drying cannot be effected osmotically. Also, another set of experiments of Raper (1940b) might have a similar explanation. He showed that an increase in temperature resulted in the cessation of migration. That is, if, during the migration phase, a culture dish was taken from a low temperature and brought to a higher one, then migration would stop. This temperature rise would, of course, lower the relative humidity which would be effective in promoting culmination. If the reverse was done, that is the temperature lowered, Raper found prolonged migration. At constant high temperature he reports short periods of migration, but we were able to show that if sufficient precautions are taken to prevent evaporation, then migration may occur for long periods up to 30°C for *D. discoideum* and 32°C for *D. mucoroides* (Bonner and Shaw, 1957).

In some recent studies Whittingham and Raper (1958) have shown that the humidity requirements of *D. polycephalum* are rather special, although in general they follow the same principle. At first they encountered great difficulty in inducing the migrating pseudoplasmodia of *D. polycephalum* to culminate at all; they continued to migrate indefinitely. By accident they found that in the presence of the mold *Dematium nigrum*, fruiting occurred readily, and by a careful analysis of this phenomenon, using solutions of different relative humidities, they were able to show that the effect of the *Dematium* could be imitated by lowering the humidity. Here again, high humidity favors migration, but culmination requires even lower relative humidities than any of the other known members of the Acrasiales.

In an experiment with *D. mucoroides* under optimum high-humidity conditions we could keep the migration going for such long periods of time that it was possible to produce greatly extended fruiting bodies—far longer than in any previous report. Our record was a length of 22 cm., and I feel sure we could better this if we had a larger culture dish. Great lengths were obtained not only with some strains of *D. mucoroides*, but also with certain strains of *D. purpureum*. *P. violaceum*, in one strain, produced lengths of 8 cm., and even some isolates of *P. pallidum* could be considerably elongated in this way. In *D. mucoroides* it is especially striking since the original cell mass is not especially large, and so with continued migration the majority of the cells enter the stalk leaving a minute sorus at the end of an absurdly long stalk.

3. The mechanism of the culmination movement

While the culmination period is a discrete and easily separable period from migration in *D. discoideum* and *D. polycephalum*, in those forms such as *D. mucoroides*, which have a stalk throughout migration, the distinction is more difficult. One simple method of solving the problem is to say that *D. mucoroides* and other continuously stalked forms have no migration periods, but culminate at the end of aggregation. The difficulty with this definition is that it ignores the striking parallels between the migration period of the stalkless forms and the equivalent period in the stalked forms. Here I have defined culmination as that period of stalk formation when the final spore differentiation takes place and when the stalk is oriented more or less at right angles to the substratum. I will be the first to admit that such a definition has the disadvantage of being imprecise (at least for *D. mucoroides* and other stalked forms), but it is hoped that with increased knowledge of the details of the changes occurring during development it will be possible to give a more rigid and sharp definition. In any event it is possible, in this way, to preserve and underscore the fact that there are two periods: one of wandering and one of rising into the air to produce mature spores. The fact that the wandering phase may be with or without stalk would appear to be of less importance.

The change in direction from a position parallel to the substratum to one at a right angle is most striking in *D. discoideum*. In *D. mucoroides* and other similar forms the long stalk will often take a right angle bend, but this is by no means invariably the case. During the migration period of both *D. discoideum* and *D. mucoroides* (as well as *Polysphondylium* and the other larger stalked species) there are, as has been discussed in detail, highly sensitive light and heat tropisms. In all these forms the same tropisms operate in a minor way during culmination. The culminating sorocarps will bend slightly towards light, but the influence is not so strong as to completely override the general upright tendency of the culmination stalk building.

Also, it is known that acrasin continues to be produced during culmination. This is especially easy to demonstrate in *D. discoideum* which has the clear-cut culmination period (Bonner, 1949). The acrasin is primarily, if not entirely, produced by the tip region; none of the posterior pre-spore (or later the spore) region shows any signs of secreting acrasin. In fact, the secreting appears not even to be accomplished by all the pre-stalk cells but only by those at the anterior end. This is especially interesting when one remembers that no cell is at the tip for very long; there is no group of dominant apical cells that remain in position, but there is a constant rotation of cells as they pass upward from the peripheral pre-stalk region and enter into the top of the stalk to become trapped there. It was shown previously that these pre-stalk cells secrete the cellulose stalk as they pass upward, and now it appears that they also give one final squirt of acrasin before they become incorporated into the stalk.

Evidence from the speed of movement exactly parallels that found for the migrating stage, namely: in *D. discoideum* large sorocarps culminate more rapidly (Bonner and El-dredge, 1945). The same argument applies here that not only the cells at the surface, but the cells inside, as well, contribute towards the movement. Culmination differs from migration in that the movement gradually tapers off to a halt as the process is completed. Gregg (1950) has examined the oxygen consumption of culminating sorocarps and finds that the oxygen consumption tapers off in an identical fashion. It is assumed that both the gradual decrease in respiration and the decrease in rate of movement reflects the decrease in the number of pre-stalk cells as they are used up in the formation of the stalk.

There is one very strong reason for discounting the possibility that the pre-spore cells are involved in the culmination movement, or that they affect the rate of the process. In *D. discoideum* differentiation into the final spores (which are encapsulated and non-motile) occurs relatively early in the rising process, and furthermore, it occurs rapidly, within an hour or less (Bonner, 1944). At the moment when this occurs there is no abrupt change in either the rate of rise or the rate of oxygen consumption. Therefore, from the evidence given so far, it would appear that the pre-spore cells are not in any major way concerned in the culmination movement; the pre-stalk cells and possibly the rear-guard cells (which have pre-stalk staining characteristics) are the remaining possibilities. Furthermore, it is inferred that it is not just the surface layer of these cells that is active, but the whole group.

To come now to the matter of how these cells with pre-stalk characteristics raise the cell mass into the air, we may first examine some arguments of Raper. In a general discussion

of stalk formation in *D. discoideum* Raper and Fennell
(1952) emphasized the fact that the cells, once they entered
the stalk, became large within a firm-walled cylinder, and
this cell expansion must provide some lifting force. Since the
upper pre-stalk cells are oriented in an oblique direction with
their long axes approximately at right angles to the direction
of movement, these authors suggested that the pre-stalk cells
are passively pushed or gathered by the cohesive, surface-
tension forces, aided perhaps by the rear-guard cells and the
pre-spores that have not yet differentiated. Once spore differentiation has occurred (and therefore the production of
slime sheath by the sorus has stopped), surface tension alone
exerts the force necessary to compress the pre-stalk zone.

However, as Raper points out (1956a, Raper and Quinlan,
1958), this explanation would hardly apply in the case of
Acytostelium which has no stalk cells at all. And furthermore,
all the cells, with the possible exception of the apical cell, are
oriented with their long axes transverse to the direction of
movement. Raper and Quinlan suggest that here the radially
oriented cells secrete the firm cellulose stalk at their central
ends, and from this support, push outward and upward. They
consider that all the movement is confined to the cells at the
terminal end, and that the remainder follows by being drawn
up by cohesive forces.

Judging from the orientation of the cells within the whole
cell mass of *Acytostelium* and from the orientation of the
cells within the tip of *Dictyostelium*, it would seem to me that
they are both moving by the same principle. The fact that the
cells are oriented at right angles to the direction of movement
does not necessarily indicate, as Raper proposes, that the cells
are not themselves pushing, and that they are simply being
passively squeezed. All the pre-stalk cells of *Dictyostelium*
and all the cells of *Acytostelium* would, I should think, be
reasonable candidates to perform the active movement of

culmination, although how they achieve this is indeed an unsolved problem. If one were to propose a hypothetical scheme somewhat different from the one proposed by Raper, it could be suggested that the forward thrust is achieved by the cells secreting slime at their posterior ends, and that by hardening, this slime provides a support for the propulsion. This notion was suggested by the striking resemblance of the oriented anterior cells to the "bottle cells" of amphibian gastrulae. As Holtfreter (1943a, b, 1944) has pointed out, the bottle cells retain a connection with the surface coat, and the same is true of slime mold cells which appear in stained sections to be attached to the external slime sheath. This explanation is therefore similar to the one proposed for the migration movement of *D. discoideum* (Fig. 12).

In culmination there is the added feature of a central stalk, and this raises the question of the relationship between the oblique cells and stalk formation. It is known from the studies of polysaccharide distribution that the stalk is being deposited by the pre-stalk cells which surround it in a columnar epithelium. There would appear, then, to be two possibilities: 1) that the pre-stalk cells exude slime sheath material at their external ends and stalk cellulose at their central ends, or 2) that the production of stalk sheath is essentially an exaggerated form of slime sheath secretion, and therefore there are two groups of cells, one active at the external surface and another at the stalk surface, both contributing to the forward push. The second possibility has the alluring feature of suggesting a common basic mechanism for both slime sheath and stalk sheath secretion. Also, it would fit in with the notion mentioned previously for migration, that the rate of movement is greatest where the slime is being deposited. In culmination there would be two such sites: the surface of the stalk and the external slime sheath surface. All the regions between these two cylinders of firm traction will move at a slower rate, giving a transverse orientation to the cells which are attached to either surface and extend inwards.

Were this hypothesis correct, then again one must assume that there is a controlling, coordinating agent which governs the direction of cell movement. It is conceivable that acrasin is involved, but there is no evidence to support this idea. There is still a long road to travel before we will have any complete understanding of the mechanics of the culmination movement.

IV. Variation and the Problem of Differentiation

ONE of the grand problems of embryology is the problem of differentiation. How is it that one fertilized egg can produce in its ontogeny, cells of all different structural and chemical compositions? It has long been argued that there may be certain substances or particles which are passed down by cleavage in some cell lines and not in others, and that this may be the *modus operandi* of differentiation. As is well known, the evidence is excellent that this is the case at certain periods in the development of many organisms, but that such an explanation is totally inadequate for regulative development. Here, all the cells retain all the potentialities of differentiation, and their fate depends, as Driesch showed many years ago, upon their position within the whole.

Because of the fact that cellular slime molds (with the exception of *Acytostelium*) differentiate into two cell types, and because they arise from aggregates of cells that have undergone their growth and most of their cell division before their aggregation, and finally because they show (as will be discussed in detail further on) remarkable powers of regulation upon cutting and fusing cell masses, these organisms provide almost ideal material to examine the mechanism of regulative development.

I should like to approach the problem from the point of view of variation. In this way one should imagine the difference between stalk and spore cells as being cell variation. But before it is possible to examine how such cell variation can arise within one organism, it is necessary to consider the variation between strains and between clones, to see which kind of variation is operating in the process of differentiation, and which variation is operating as fodder for natural selection. The point is that since aggregation can bring together cells of different genetic constitutions, one may have fruiting bodies of mixed genotypes. This, it will be shown, is more likely important in terms of natural selection and adaptation in the species than it is to the process of differentiation. On the other hand, if a sorocarp comes originally from one cell which first multiplies and then aggregates, the differentiation arises within a mass of cells which are genetically equivalent, yet despite this equivalence there is ample evidence of cell variability. The final question that will concern us here is whether or not this variation can be harnessed to contribute to differentiation. This chapter will be divided into three sections in which the variations between species and strains, between clones, and between the cells within a clone will be examined in succession.

1. Variation between species and strains

One way to study the variation between species and strains is to mix the cells at different stages of development and observe the degree of compatibility. The mixing of cells of different species, particularly at the feeding or vegetative stage, was first done by Olive (1902). He mixed *D. mucoroides* and *D. purpureum* and found that they produce their characteristic fruiting bodies side by side, showing no coalescence. This matter was thoroughly investigated by Raper and Thom (1941), who not only confirmed Olive's findings, but far extended the observations. They showed that by mixing spores or the vegetative amoebae, *D. discoideum* and *P. violaceum* would aggregate separately; mixtures of *D. discoideum* and *D. mucoroides* formed common aggregations, but separate fruiting bodies appeared at the center. Grafts during the migration stage showed some temporary merging in the combination of *D. discoideum* and *D. purpureum*.

Furthermore, they found that these two species would form a unified fruiting body when their migrating cell masses were thoroughly intermixed, although spores from this hybrid sorocarp produced, in the F_2, separate sorocarps characteristic of each species.

Gregg (1956) has pursued this matter of adhesion between cells by injecting amoebae of different species into rabbits and obtaining antibodies. He found that the antibodies were species specific on vegetative amoebae, but that this was not the case once the aggregation stage was reached. On the basis of these experiments he suggests that a general tendency for surface adhesion appears at the migration stage, thereby possibly explaining the observation of Raper and Thom (1941) that the combining of *D. discoideum* and *D. purpureum* cells can only take place at later stages of development. It is, of course, difficult to know to what extent Gregg's experiments reflect the normal properties of cell adhesion, for there is no doubt, as Shaffer (1957a, b) has shown, that stickiness plays an important role in both the aggregation and the later cell association phases. He demonstrated that in combinations of cells of different species there is both a variation in the amount of stickiness depending upon the combination, as well as the possibility of species-specific acrasins playing an important part in the coalescence of the cells of different species.

If we now turn to the variation between strains, we will find, as has been pointed out on numerous occasions, that each isolate of a cellular slime mold made from nature is likely to show some recognizable morphological characteristic that gives it a distinctive appearance. This is especially evident in the case of *D. mucoroides*, no doubt because it is so frequently isolated. A convenient way of revealing some of the more obvious strain differences is to culture them on a low nutrient agar toward a light source. Some strains are small and show little migration while others will migrate for long periods. Additional differences that have appeared in our cultures are a tendency to form a wavy stalk, tendencies toward periods of stalkless migration, occasional branching, slight differences in PAS staining reactions, presence or absence of macrocysts (Blaskovics and Raper, 1957), a characteristic form to the migrating mass, and a number of more doubtful, less conspicuous ones. These differences are never of sufficient importance to argue for separate species, with the possible exception of size, for *D. minutum* (Raper, 1941a) is perhaps only an extremely small form of *D. mucoroides*.[1]

Recently we have run a series of experiments in which the cells of these various strains of *D. mucoroides* are mixed, and we find the surprising result that for the most part, the cells fail to come together, as though they were separate species (Bonner and Adams, 1958). These experiments were extended to include other species as well, and in some instances different species did fuse, while many combinations of different strains of the same species did not. Moreover, there were differences in the nature of the combinations showing varying degrees of fusion and compatibility.

The cells were mixed in two different ways, for the most part showing the same results. In one method the aggregating center of one strain was put in among the aggregation streams of another after the center of the latter had been removed. The second method consisted of mixing the cells of two migrating masses very thoroughly with an eyelash.

Depending upon the strains used, the results could be put in one of three categories of compatibility: 1) In the extreme case there is a complete separation of the cells to form two

[1] On the upper end of the size scale Singh (1947a) has proposed a *D. giganteum*, but the difficulty is that the size range is almost continuous in different isolates of *D. mucoroides* between medium-sized ones and the largest. *D. minutum* is very much smaller than any other *D. mucoroides*, which favors Raper's (1941a) view that it is a separate species.

separate fruiting bodies. 2) In the intermediate case there is a partial merger; the two discrete cell masses adhere to one another during the migration stage, but they culminate separately, one standing on the sorus of the other. If in these instances the cells are thoroughly mixed, then the cells will re-group during the migration stage so that each strain will be one cohesive mass. 3) The highest degree of compatibility found so far is shown in some masses where there is a single sorus containing two homogeneous, discrete patches of pre-spores, each belonging to one of the strains. Since the cells in this third case do still pull apart and re-group, there is obviously some incompatibility, and theoretically it should be possible to find two strains that are completely compatible in which the spores of both will be spread at random throughout one common sorus.

This matter of sorting out is now a well recognized phenomenon in experiments with dissociated animal cells. I shall not enter here upon a detailed history of the discovery of the phenomenon; the original idea stems from the work of H. V. Wilson (1907), who pushed sponges through bolting cloth and noted that the dissociated cells reorganized to form new functional sponges. He made the incorrect assumption, at the time of his original experiment, that the differentiated cells had reverted back to some embryonic type and then redifferentiated following coalescence. This error was first corrected by J. S. Huxley (1911, 1921), who worked with another species of sponge and showed that the different cells retain their differentiation following dissociation. He pointed out that Driesch's dictum (that the fate of a cell is the function of its position) does not hold in this case; it is in fact the reverse, for the position of a cell is a function of its differentiation. That is, the differentiated cells wander about in the coalesced clump of dissociated cells until they find their proper location. This point has been confirmed in numerous ways by different workers; and is excellently reviewed by P. Brien (1937) who has contributed some evidence himself.

Much the same story can be told of the dissociation of Coelenterate cells, and more recently there have been some remarkably convincing experiments on dissociated vertebrate cells. In 1952 Weiss and Andres injected dissociated presumptive melanoblasts into the blood stream of chick embryos, and they found that these cells became lodged in their appropriate region in the embryo. Townes and Holtfreter (1955) were able to show such specific reorganization in dissociated amphibian embryos, although the best evidence that the cells retain their differentiations comes from recent work. In particular, Trinkaus (1957) has been able to follow the cell types using isotope markers, and Moscona (1957) has used an elegant method with a mixture of cells from different species. Previously he had developed a method of dissociating cells by the use of trypsin, and then to mark his cells he used combinations of chick and mouse cells, each of which is histologically recognizable. If mouse and chick cartilage are mixed, a mass of continuous cartilage results in which there is a random distribution of mouse and chick cartilage cells. However, if mouse cartilage cells are mixed with chick kidney cells then the cells by migration form discrete groups of a mass of cartilage and a mass of kidney tissue. The important proof is that all the cartilage is mouse and all the kidney is chick; there has been no cell transformation but merely a regrouping of the cells.

It should be noted that these experiments of Moscona differ from the slime mold experiments reported here, in that his cells showed no specificity in their regrouping with respect to species but only with respect to the tissue. In the slime molds the cells show species specificities in their regrouping, but we have not yet found anything akin to tissue regroupings. The cells remain totipotent until the last moment before final differentiation. If we were to draw a conclusion from this paradox, it is, perhaps, that the common denominator in this interesting process of sorting out or regrouping is not the degree of differentiation or determination of the cells, but rather the degree of surface compatibility among the cells. Cells which are completely compatible will mix randomly; cells which are completely incompatible will separate completely; cells which show in intermediate degree of surface compatibility will regroup by sorting out.[2] This intermediate degree of surface compatibility may be produced either by species differences, as in the slime molds, or by differences in cell differentiation, as in vertebrate cells. Moreover, in the case of sponges this incompatibility can be produced both ways, for Galtsoff (1929) showed that in mixtures of cells of different sponges there was both a sorting out with respect to differentiation and a sorting out with respect to species.

Our intention in this chapter is to assess the roles of various kinds of variations and to discern whether the variation plays a part in selection or whether it contributes to differentiation. The variation between species and strains certainly must provide the material for selection, although we may fail completely at the moment to understand what traits have advantages in any particular environmental circumstance. One might assume the incompatibility between strains to be an isolating mechanism, operating from an evolutionary point of view just like the sexual incompatibility systems of higher organisms. Here, instead of gametes being unable to fuse, the cells are unable to aggregate in a common mass. In this way it is possible for separate species to arise, for without some such compatibility barriers it would be

[2] There is also the possibility in the slime molds that the grouping is affected by the speed of cells, the fast ones taking an anterior position and the slow ones lagging behind.

most difficult to preserve variations and allow evolutionary progress.

Strain and species differences, however, can hardly contribute to the differentiation of spore and stalk cells within any one individual. We may, nevertheless, from the experiments on the re-grouping of cells, have some clues that might be important to differentiation. Cells can wander freely through the mass and stick selectively one to another, and it is conceivable that within the cell population of one individual, cell regrouping could play a role in differentiation. This point will be considered more carefully in the discussion of the variation within a clone.

2. Variation within a strain

The problem of variation in cellular slime molds has been studied intensively by Sussman and his group. He was the first to exploit the fact that by the study of variation it might be possible to gain some insight into the problem of development. Some of his experiments have dealt with the problem of variation within a clone (which will be considered in the next section), while others concern the behavior of variants induced within a strain.

With the use of ultraviolet light and the isolation of single cells, he and his co-workers have produced an array of mutant forms of *D. discoideum, D. mucoroides*, and *D. purpureum* (Sussman and Sussman, 1953; Sussman, 1955a; see also three reviews by Sussman, 1955b, 1956b, Sussman and Sussman, 1956). They fall into two general categories: either they stop at some specific stage before culmination (because of a failure to aggregate, for instance), or they culminate with the fruiting body abnormal in character. For the most part, a careful analysis of the morphology and development of these abnormal sorocarps is wanting, although the general character of the different mutants obtained by Sussman can be put easily into one of the following classifications:

1. Aggregateless. The growth is normal but no aggregation takes place. All three species irradiated give aggregateless mutants with considerable frequency; this is the most commonly observed aberration. There is considerable variation among the particular aggregateless mutants, indicating that the same change is not induced each time. The type of medium affects the extent of the expression of the mutant character; none aggregate on a rich nutrient medium, but if the amoebae are centrifuged free of bacteria and placed on washed agar, some of the aggregateless forms proceed to the beginning of aggregation, and others continue through to the end (Sussman, 1954). Aggregateless mutants were first reported by Pfützner-Eckert (1950), who observed them appearing spontaneously in her cultures.

2. Fruitless. These forms undergo aggregation and then stop, leaving a mound of cells. They appear to be less affected by the culture conditions and are relatively stable.

3. Bushy. There is normal aggregation with these mutants, but instead of forming one center, the cell masses break up into numerous small papillae, each one of which produces a small, often highly irregular fruiting body. In so doing, they resemble some of the small forms of cellular slime molds, for *D. lacteum* and *D. minutum* will, under favorable culture conditions, break up into a series of smaller fruiting bodies. This raises the interesting point that size in the slime molds can be regulated both by the number of amoebae that enter an aggregate and by the number of sorocarps formed by an aggregate. It is conceivable, also, that there is some relation between this phenomenon and the delayed break-up into small sorocarps found in *D. polycephalum* and *Polysphondylium*.

4. Glassy. This mutant form is normal up to culmination,

and during culmination it produces a thick structure showing no obvious demarcation between stalk and spore regions.

5. Forked. This is somewhat similar to glassy, except that at the tip of the thick, straight stalks there are usually twin sori produced.

6. Dwarf and Fruity. These mutants are normal morphologically, the only alteration being their minute size. This is especially marked in the mutant Fruity of *D. discoideum*, where an aggregate may consist of very few cells (Plate VIII).

There are a number of other mutants listed by Sussman (1956b) including some that involve the pigmentation of the spore mass (in *D. discoideum*), and two further aberrations during culmination: Curly and Long-Stemmed (in *D. mucoroides*).

Since these altered forms are stable through many successive generations, it is Sussman's view that they represent genetic mutants in the classic sense. With the use of these mutants Sussman has been able to make two valuable contributions:

One has already been discussed; it concerns the mixing of these mutants in different combinations at all different stages of development to gain evidence for recombination and sexuality. It is, from the genetic point of view, a great pity that these attempts were unsuccessful, but they do cast serious doubt on the possibility of at least certain kinds of sexual systems postulated for the Acrasiales.

Sussman's other contribution is the use of the mutants to analyze the steps leading to development. He was able to show that by mixing particular combinations of two mutants that were unable to complete their development (aggregateless and fruitless) there was in some cases a synergistic reaction, and that development proceeded farther than would have been the case normally for either one alone (Sussman, 1954). For example, it is possible to mix Fruitless-1, which normally forms loose aggregates, with Aggregateless-53, which never aggregates, and the result will be normal, mature fruiting bodies. He has a dozen or so cases of such synergism, and curiously enough, one case of antagonism.[3] The stock Aggregateless-208 can aggregate on washed agar but not on the normal nutrient medium. However, on washed agar, in the presence of Aggregateless-206, it fails to aggregate. This effect is specific and can occur even after the Aggregateless-206 cells has been killed by a heat treatment.

Sussman adopted the reasonable hypothesis that the normal development of the mutants was blocked at some enzymatic step, and that by a kind of syntropy or cross feeding, these necessary syntheses were by-passed by the presence of another mutant that could produce the needed substances. The next step was to determine whether or not these substances were diffusible, and this was done by constructing very fine agar membranes and putting the two mutants on opposite sides (Sussman and Lee, 1955). It is most unfortunate that in no case was there any evidence of synergism across the membrane; each mutant developed as though it were alone, although as Runyon (1942) had reported previously, the acrasin readily passed through the membrane. From this Sussman is forced to the unhappy conclusion that these key substances, of which we are so eager to learn more, must be passed directly by cell contact, a fact which will make their elucidation more difficult.

In the study of these variations within a strain, the question arises as to what part they normally play in nature. Unfortunately we know nothing of the normal mutation rate, but recently in our laboratory Filosa (1958) has opened up a whole new view of the problem of variation within cellular

[3] This kind of antagonism was first reported by Pfützner-Eckert (1950).

slime molds. He has discovered that any one strain or isolate of a cellular slime mold (which has been repeatedly recultured by the mass transfer of spores) is not usually made up of one genetic cell strain, but of two or more. That is, if he makes careful single-spore platings from the fruiting bodies of a particular isolate, they will show that the majority of the spores give rise to colonies identical in appearance with the parent, but a certain per cent of the cells will produce colonies that are distinctly different. This point is implicit in an experiment of Blaskovics and Raper (1957), where they show that the macrocyst-producing character is different in different clones of a particular strain of *D. mucoroides*; further, Sussman (1956b) makes the brief remark that mutants have been found in unirradiated populations of *D. mucoroides*. However, to Filosa goes the credit of appreciating how widespread the phenomenon is, and how many cells of a fruiting body of a particular strain can be of an aberrant type.

To give an example, he finds in our strain No. 11 of *D. mucoroides* that in single spore isolates roughly 87 per cent resemble the parent, and 13 per cent have distinctly different appearances which fall into three categories: The most common (which averages approximately 9 per cent) is a form in which the migration period is without a stalk. It does not really resemble *D. discoideum*, for the cell masses are messy and irregular, frequently disintegrating and breaking up into separate amoebae. Also, it has no basal disc, and histological preparations of the migrating stage show a few abortive stalk cells in the tip region of the abnormally pointed migrating mass. Occasionally one finds clones that differ from the parent stock in that they have a reduced period of migration and a peculiar aggregation pattern which is somehow slowed down so that aggregation proceeds well into culmination and there is a rope of cells leading up the stalk to the rising cell mass.

Finally, aggregateless mutants appear in less than 1 per cent of the cells.

Some of these changes are very stable, for in the case of the mutant that appears in about 9 per cent of the cells, Filosa showed that this proportion is very roughly retained, at least until the 25th generation. However in other cases new mutants will appeal; in a clone derived from one "normal" or "wild type" spore of *D. mucoroides*, after 20 generations of mass spore inoculation the spores in a sorus were found to consist of almost 50 per cent of a new mutant. This was especially interesting in that the phenotype showed no indication of the mutant form, despite the fact that half its cells were of abnormal genotype.

To determine the effect of the stalkless migration clone (henceforth referred to as MV) on the normal cells of strain No. 11 of *D. mucoroides*, Filosa mixed the two cells in different proportions at various stages; he mixed spores, centrifuged vegetative amoebae, and made grafts at the aggregation stage. In this way he could vary at will the number of MV to normal cells and even test the resultant ratio in the sorus of the mixed sorocarp. In brief, he could provide 50 per cent or more MV cells, and the fruiting bodies will be normal in appearance, showing spore ratios which unexpectedly will be predominately MV (in the order of 6 to 1 in favor of MV). This would indicate either that by entering aggregations sooner there is a predominance of MV cells in the masses, or that the cell mass contains 50 per cent normal cells which have mostly gone into the formation of the typical stalk. At the moment, the facts on this point are unknown, although it is of interest that Filosa showed that if a migrating mass is made by grafting an MV tip into the aggregation streams of normal cells (or vice-versa), the result is a normal fruiting body. In other words, if there are large numbers of cells of each cell type, again the phenotypic effect of the normal cells is expressed.

If strains of cellular slime molds as they appear in nature are normally made up of two or more divergent cell types, one may well ask what might be the selective advantage of such a system. I have discussed this point in detail elsewhere (Bonner, 1958), and here I shall merely mention it briefly. The idea is that by gathering a number of cells of different genetic constitutions and bringing them together in one fruiting structure, one has, in some respects, an effective substitute for sexuality. It might be compared directly to the situation in the imperfect fungi where the nuclei of different genetic make-up will exist in one common mycelium, and these nuclei will be segregated in different combinations in the conidia. Such nuclear aggregation or heterocaryosis has the advantage over true sexuality in that there can be more than two parents, but it has the disadvantage that it lacks the rich source of chromosome recombination provided by nuclear fusion and meiosis. Of course, the perfect Ascomycetes have both a sexual system and this alternative to sex, and it may well be that some day sexuality will be demonstrated in the Acrasiales.

The cellular slime molds differ from the fungi in that the association is not of nuclei within a common cytoplasm but of cells bound together by intimate contact one with another, and for this condition the term "heterocytosis" has been proposed. This difference in no way alters the argument, and if we apply it to the case of strain No. 11 of *D. mucoroides*, we could consider that the MV and other aberrant cells are recessives, although instead of carrying the recessives in homologous chromosomes in a diploid nucleus (as in sexual organisms), or in haploid nuclei swimming in a common cytoplasm (as in heterocaryotic fungi), they are carried as separate haploid cells. Along with recessive characters in general, it may not necessarily be true that any particular one has selective advantage, but by having a mechanism by which recessives may be retained in the heterocyton, the organism has that many more potentialities to cope with environmental changes. This alternative to sexuality with its power of retaining recessive traits would provide a means whereby the slime molds could effectively evolve and meet changing conditions.

A good illustration of this point is the character of macrocyst production found in certain clones of *D. mucoroides* by Blaskovics and Raper (1957). We have a strain of this species in our laboratory which Filosa found to contain, upon single spore isolation, some cells which produced macrocysts when grown clonally. We have also shown, as mentioned previously, that these resistant macrocysts are capable of forming under a layer of water. If, now, this particular strain lands in a marshy area, or if there is a lengthy rainy season, then the strain possessing a few of these "recessive" macrocyst-producing cells can effectively take over and permit the survival and perpetuation of the species in these adverse conditions. It would be most worth while to test, by selection experiments, the validity of such a hypothesis.

Concerning the application of the experiments of Filosa to the problem of development of one individual, there is the interesting fact that the morphology of the mass can be determined by a particular cell type that makes up 50 per cent of the cell population or less (in some cases as few as 10 per cent of the wild type cells will give the wild type phenotype). Of how this is achieved, nothing is known, and one might wonder whether here also there might be some synergism as Sussman found with his mutants. Filosa has run tests parallel to those of Sussman with pure MV cells on one side of a membrane and pure normal cells on the other, and there is, as Sussman found, no transforming effect across the membrane.

But we must never lose sight of the fact that a normal fruiting body can result from the growth of one cell, one pure genetic strain; a mixture of genomes is not necessary to produce differentiation into stalk and spore cells. It is therefore appropriate in this discussion of differentiation to examine the variation within a clone.

3. Variation within a clone

Skupienski (1920) was the first to isolate a single spore (in *D. mucoroides*) and show that normal fruiting bodies would result after a period of growth. This has been confirmed by Raper (1951) and myself (Bonner, 1952) for *D. discoideum*, and Sussman (1951) did an extensive series of experiments substantiating the notion. He also showed that single vegetative cells are capable of giving rise to whole colonies, although his data for the cells at the later stages of association are less convincing, for it is not clear that he did in fact separate the sticky masses of cells. But since aggregating and migrating cells may be made to revert back to vegetative cells, there is no reason to doubt that any cell, except those that have been trapped in the stalk for some time, have the power of starting a new colony upon isolation. The reason for arguing that the stalk cells lose this capacity is that there is good evidence that the stalk cells slowly degenerate and die.[4]

If a sorocarp may arise from a single cell, we are faced with the problem of how this one cell produces both stalk and spore cells. Furthermore, it does so by first producing a large number of independent cells that then stream together into masses. The first question that must be answered is whether

[4] See page 51.

or not these separate vegetative cells, just prior to aggregation, are totipotent (or dipotent in this case since they can only become spores or stalk cells). The other possibility is that they have already become segregated in their character, and that they assemble in aggregation according to their future role.

This question has been partially answered by a classical experiment of Raper (1940b). He cut the migrating slug of *D. discoideum* into fractions and noted that each fraction produced a normal fruiting body containing both stalk and spore cells (Fig. 13). The anterior fraction was special, in that it took a period of migration before the proportions were normal; regulation in the tip takes more time, and if the culmination occurred right after the operation, the sorocarp had a disproportionately thick stalk and a small sorus. Given enough time, any cell which was previously destined to become a stalk cell may be made to turn into a spore, and vice versa. Therefore, the cells during the migration phase are totipotent in the sense that they are capable of shifting their fates according to their position within the mass.

A further insight into this problem was given by repeating this experiment of Raper's and sectioning and staining the cut fractions by the periodic acid-Schiff method (Bonner, Chiquoine, and Kolderine, 1955). The results showed that an anterior fraction which previously had the characteristic staining of pre-stalk would slowly change at the posterior end so that ultimately it would have a pre-spore and pre-stalk zone. The opposite was equally true of the posterior end, showing that the cytological peculiarities of pre-stalk and pre-spore are reversible.

Not only in these cutting experiments but normally, there is a great range in size of the fruiting bodies, depending upon how many amoebae enter an aggregation. As Raper (1935) noted in his original description of *D. discoideum*, the fruit-

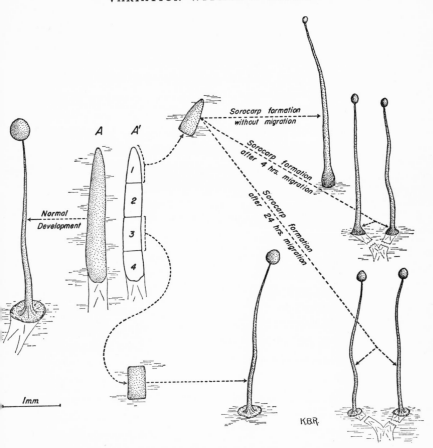

Fig. 13. Comparison of the fruiting of entire cell masses of *Dictyostelium discoideum* with different fractions of the same. If apical fractions fruit immediately they show abnormal proportions, but with some migration the normal proportions are resumed. (From Raper, 1940b.)

ing bodies are all roughly proportionate in their ratios of stalk to spore cells. The matter has been substantiated in detail for *D. discoideum* (Bonner and Slifkin, 1949). Harper (1926, 1929, 1932) was struck by the same fact for *D. mucoroides* and *Polysphondylium*. Because the stalk and sorus are of such different shapes and constitutions, the technical problem of comparing the sizes of the two has always been great, but by measuring the pre-stalk and pre-spore areas it is now possible to obtain a far more satisfactory picture of the nature of this proportionate relationship (Bonner, 1958).

In *D. discoideum* there is a linear relationship between the values for the volume of the pre-stalk and pre-spore zones. In *D. mucoroides* the relationship is non-linear, but if plotted logarithmically the relation is linear or allometric. In this way it is possible to compare the two species on the same graph.

There are two obvious differences which are of interest. One is that the pre-stalk zone is relatively larger in *D. discoideum*. Since this species does not produce a stalk during migration, I have argued that the two phenomena are correlated, and that perhaps the pre-stalk zone is large because no stalk is being constructed. This point will be pursued shortly. The other difference between the two species is that in *D. discoideum* the division line stays approximately the same throughout migration, but in *D. mucoroides* stalk cells are constantly being used up at the tip. Since the proportions will fall on the allometric curve, no matter where the cell mass is in its migration period, one must conclude that as migration proceeds and as the cells disappear from the tip into the stalk, the division line slowly recedes to keep the proportions exact; *D. mucoroides* is constantly undergoing regulation as it migrates. In this way, in one of the masses that has migrated 20 or more centimeters, the cell mass in the beginning will have a huge pre-spore zone, but by the end it will be minute as will be the final sorus, for almost all the cells have gone into the stalk.

We have now, with this description of proportions and regulation, some understanding of what needs to be explained. One cell can produce a mass of cells by growth, and these cells are all totipotent, yet when they come together by aggregation some cells turn into the stalk and others into the spore mass. In attempting a further attack on the problem, let us examine the cell variability within this clone with greater care. The fact that the cells are totipotent hardly means that they are similar in all respects; it only means they retain spore and stalk cell potentialities. Are there other differences within this clonal population and could such differences be playing a role in differentiation?

One attempt to show such differences is that of Sussman (reviewed by Sussman, 1956b) in the tests for his hypothesis that in aggregation there were two kinds of cells: responder and initiator cells. As has already been mentioned, from his most recent work on this subject Sussman (1956a) comes to the conclusion that there is no special genetic change, and that cells which are first involved in the aggregation are not unique but probably show some quantitative difference from the others, which permits them to arrive at the aggregative state sooner. Therefore, although this rules against any kind of special "queen bee" or initiator cell, it does show that the cells vary with respect to the time they start aggregation; and some begin earlier than others.

The most obvious variation in the cells is one of size, for the size range of both cells and nuclei in the different stages of development is unusually high (Bonner and Frascella, 1953; Bonner, Chiquoine, and Kolderie, 1955). This may be seen especially dramatically if the size range of *Dictyostelium* cells is compared with the range of different unicellular organism as listed by Adolph (1931); there is little that approaches the variability of the cells of the slime mold.

Recently we have performed some preliminary experiments to see if cell size may be inherited, along the lines of Johannsen's famous experiments on selection for size in beans and Jenning's (1941) experiments on selection in *Difflugia*. The procedure was to first take a strain of *D. mucoroides* and measure the frequency distribution of spore size for 100 spores. Then single spores were isolated and measured, after which the spore was allowed to produce an F_1 generation.[5] The size range of this generation was measured, and in no case did the range differ significantly from the range of the parental strains, even where the original spore of the clone was on the large or the small end of the range. Admittedly, to make these experiments even more convincing this should be repeated over a series of generations, but as they now stand, they are sufficient to justify the statement that the size of the parent cell does not affect either the mean size or the variability of its progeny. The variation in size within a clone is independent of the size of the parent cell. What is inherited is the ability to have great size variation, and this is not determined by the size of any one cell.

Another clear-cut variation in the cell population is that of speed of movement.[6] It is an easy matter to show that the aggregating cells vary greatly in their rate of movement, and I have already given the evidence that all cells do not move at the same speed in the migration stage.[7] Also, it will be recalled that by grafting vitally colored anterior portions into colorless posterior portions it could be shown that they moved anteriorly as a group of cells, while posterior cells placed anteriorly lagged, finally settling at the hind end (Bonner, 1952). This suggested that either before or during migration there was a sorting out of fast and slow cells, the fast ones

[5] This was done by using modifications of a technique of Lederberg (1954). The spores in suspension were drawn up into a small pipette and dispensed in minute drops onto a slide. The slide was marked off in squares and covered with a layer of heavy mineral oil. Then each drop was examined with a microscope for those with only one spore. The spore was measured and transferred to an environment favorable for growth.

[6] It is not known if the speed of an individual cell is correlated with its size; it would be most interesting to examine this point.

[7] See page 93.

populating the front end, the slow ones, the hind end. Subsequent work has indicated that this major sorting out takes
place at the end of aggregation, and that during migration
there are only a few especially fast and especially slow cells
that continue to change their relative positions (Bonner,
1957; Bonner and Adams, 1958).

Experiments have also been performed to determine
whether or not this difference in velocity is inherited (Bonner, 1952). Anterior ends of migrating slugs of D. discoideum, which presumably contained all fast cells, were cut
off and allowed to fruit. The spores of these fruiting bodies
were sown on fresh media, and a migrating slug of the next
generation was again cut so that its anterior end fruited.
This was repeated for ten generations, but even after this
continued selection the fruiting bodies that arose from this
long line of especially fast spores showed no differences in
their speed of migration, or any other character, from a
normal population of D. discoideum. This was repeated for
the posterior end with the same results. Therefore speed, as
was the case with size, is not affected by the speed of the
parent cells; what is passed on by any one cell, fast or slow,
is the ability to produce cells of different rates of movement.

However, in discussing the size and the velocity of cells,
we have only described their characters in greater detail, as
well as given evidence as to their mode of inheritance. We
have not yet answered the question of whether differences
within a clone play a role in differentiation. The only hint
given so far that this might be the case is that the variability
stemming from one cell is of such a magnitude that it is
difficult to imagine that it is not harnessed in some way.

There certainly are indications that the cells with different
rates of movement are randomly placed during the vegetative
stage, but by the end of aggregation they have become organized so that not only are they all moving in the same direc-

tion, but the fast cells are in front and the slow cells behind. If this is a sound observation it indicates that right in the beginning of the organization of the mass there are cell differences between the front and the hind ends.[8] These differences will inevitably produce a gradient, although we are a far cry from having any exact idea of the chemical or functional character of this gradient. It would mean, perhaps also, that fast cells have a tendency to move in the pre-stalk direction, and slow cells, in the pre-spore direction, although this condition is at all times reversible, as the experiments on cell potency have shown. But this last statement brings us onto dangerous ground, for the problem of proportions cannot be ignored; more than that, perhaps the key to the explanation of differentiation lies in the explanation of proportions.

As I have pointed out elsewhere, the fact that there is a proportionate relationship between pre-stalk and pre-spore cells, and the fact that this relation comes to a new equilibrium when a piece of the cell mass is excised, must mean that there is some kind of communication between the parts (Bonner, 1957). To put the matter in crude terms, a front cell "knows" how many cells there are behind, and its fate will be decided accordingly. This implies communication; what is communicated is the approximate number of cells, but how it is communicated is, of course, completely unknown. It may be profitable to make a few hypotheses to see what kind of an explanation would satisfy.

We know that within the migrating slug all the cells are moving in the same direction. There is evidence for numerous special qualities in the tip, such as the fact that it produces

[8] In some recent unpublished experiments I have been able to show that if a migrating pseudoplasmodium is cut into two sections and each half allowed to fruit, the spores from the anterior half are highly significantly larger that the spores from the posterior half. This is convincing evidence that during aggregation the larger cells go to the front end of the developing pseudoplasmodium.

more acrasin than any other portion. Also, Raper (1940b) showed in an interesting experiment that if supplementary tips are grafted onto the side of a migrating pseudoplasmodium, the cells within are portioned out so that each supplementary tip and the original tip have equal shares, producing a number of small, separate pseudoplasmodia corresponding in number to the number of tips. The tip then is a dominant center, in the sense of C. M. Child (1941). However, we cannot as yet know whether this dominance is achieved by the fact that there are more "fast" cells in the front end.

From all this we might assume that there is a special reaction taking place at the tip. Now let us further assume that the intensity of this reaction is limited by some substance— possibly a simple substrate that is brought from the posterior region. This would be the messenger necessary for the communication between the parts, for the greater the posterior cell mass, the greater the quantity of the substance that can be brought forward in a polar fashion. The only obvious things that we can see moving forward are the especially fast moving cells, and one could postulate that these are bringing the necessary substances. The larger the cell mass, the more especially fast cells continuously move forward, dumping their substance into the reaction of the dominant tip.

This hypothesis also fits the fact that the pre-stalk region in *D. mucoroides* is small compared to *D. discoideum*. If one assumes that the anterior reaction leads to both stalk formation and the production of the pre-spore character, then in *D. discoideum*, since no stalk is formed during migration, all the effect can be concentrated on the production of pre-stalk cells, which results in a larger, more conspicuous zone.

Such speculation soon becomes hollow and unrewarding; the time has come to test these hypotheses and just as likely replace them on the basis of newly discovered facts. I have dwelt on them here only to show what kind of an answer could explain this highly controlled and proportional differentiation—this fine example of regulative development.

The idea that the genetically identical cells of a clone may vary (that is the ability to vary is the character that is inherited) and, that this variability is then exploited and organized to produce the coordinated pattern of the cellular slime molds, has the merit of fitting in with our concept of development in other conventional organisms. For, after all, the cell progeny of a fertilized egg may in some multicellular animal or plant remain totipotent for long periods of development, yet clearly organized differences do arise, and these differences could indeed involve the controlled exploitation of clonal cell variation. In both cases we still seek deeper insight into the method of control; we are still many experiments away from any complete understanding.

Bibliography

THE lists of references are divided into two parts. First, there is a complete list of all those books and articles which have made a significant contribution to the biology of the Acrasiales up through 1957 (with many references in 1958). Abstracts and theses are not included unless the material has not appeared in a printed article. The second list is of those references that are mentioned in the text but are not concerned primarily with the cellular slime molds.

A Bibliography of the Cellular Slime Molds

Arndt, A. (1937). Untersuchungen über *Dictyostelium muco-roides* Brefeld. *Roux' Arch. Entwickl. 136*, 681-747.

Blaskovics, J. C. and K. B. Raper (1957). Encystment stages of *Dictyostelium. Biol. Bull. 113*, 58-88.

Bonner, J. T. (1944). A descriptive study of the development of the slime mold *Dictyostelium discoideum. Amer. J. Bot. 31*, 175-182.

Bonner, J. T. (1947). Evidence for the formation of cell aggregates by chemotaxis in the development of the slime mold *Dictyostelium discoideum. J. Exp. Zool. 106*, 1-26.

Bonner, J. T. (1949). The demonstration of acrasin in the later stages of the development of the slime mold *Dictyostelium discoideum. J. Exp. Zool. 110*, 259-271.

Bonner, J. T. (1950). Observations on polarity in the slime mold *Dictyostelium discoideum. Biol. Bull. 99*, 143-151.

Bonner, J. T. (1952). The pattern of differentiation in amoeboid slime molds. *Amer. Nat. 86*, 79-89.

Bonner, J. T. (1957). A theory of the control of differentiation in the cellular slime molds. *Quart. Rev. Biol. 32*, 232-246.

Bonner, J. T. (1958). *The Evolution of Development.* Cambridge University Press.

Bonner, J. T. and M. S. Adams (1958). Cell mixtures of different species and strains of cellular slime molds. *J. Embryol. Exp. Morph. 6*, 346-356.

Bonner, J. T., A. D. Chiquoine, and M. Q. Kolderie (1955). A histochemical study of differentiation in the cellular slime molds. *J. Exp. Zool. 130,* 133-158.

Bonner, J. T., W. W. Clark, Jr., C. L. Neely, Jr., and M. K. Slifkin (1950). The orientation to light and the extremely sensitive orientation to temperature gradients in the slime mold *Dictyostelium discoideum. J. Cell. Comp. Physiol. 36,* 149-158.

Bonner, J. T. and D. Eldredge, Jr. (1945). A note on the rate of morphogenetic movement in the slime mold *Dictyostelium discoideum. Growth 9,* 287-297.

Bonner, J. T. and E. B. Frascella (1952). Mitotic activity in relation to differentiation in the slime mold *Dicytostelium discoideum. J. Exp. Zool. 121,* 561-571.

Bonner, J. T. and E. B. Frascella (1953). Variations in cell size during the development of the slime mold *Dictyostelium discoideum. Biol. Bull. 104,* 297-300.

Bonner, J. T., P. G. Koontz, and D. Paton (1953). Size in relation to the rate of migration in the slime mold *Dictyostelium discoideum. Mycologia 45,* 235-240.

Bonner, J. T. and M. J. Shaw (1957). The role of humidity in the differentiation of the cellular slime molds. *J. Cell. Comp. Physiol. 50,* 145-154.

Bonner, J. T. and M. K. Slifkin (1949). A study of the control of differentiation: the proportions of stalk and spore cells in the slime mold *Dictyostelium discoideum. Amer. J. Bot. 36,* 727-734.

Bradley, S. G. and M. Sussman (1952). Growth of ameboid slime molds in one-membered cultures. *Arch. Biochem. Biophys. 39,* 462-463.

Bradley, S. G., M. Sussman, and H. L. Ennis (1956). Environmental factors affecting the aggregation of the cellular slime mold, *Dictyostelium discoideum. J. Protozool. 3,* 33-38.

Brefeld, O. (1869). *Dictyostelium mucoroides.* Ein neuer Organismus aus der Verwandschaft der Myxomyceten. *Abh. Senckenberg. Naturf. Ges. Frankfort 7,* 85-107.

Brefeld, O. (1884). *Polysphondylium violaceum* und *Dictyostelium mucoroides* nebst Bemerkungen zur Systematik der Schleimpilze. *Untersuchungen aus dem Gesammtgebiet der Mykologie 6,* 1-34.

Chatton, E. (1912). Entamibe (*Loeschia* sp.) et Myxomycète

(*Dictyostelium mucoroides* Brefeld) d'un Singe. *Bull. Soc. Pathologie Exotique 5*, 180-184.

Cienkowsky, L. (1873). *Guttulina rosea*. Trans. bot. section 4th meeting Russian naturalists at Kazan (in Russian).

Cohen, A. L. (1953a). The effect of ammonia on morphogenesis in the Acrasieae. *Proc. Nat. Acad. Sci. 39*, 68-74.

Cohen, A. L. (1953b). The isolation and culture of opsimorphic organisms. I. Occurrence and isolation of opsimorphic organisms from soil and culture of Acrasieae on a standard medium. *Ann. N.Y. Acad. Sci. 56*, 938-943.

Cook, W. R. I. (1939). Some observations on *Sappinia pedata* Dang. *Trans. British Mycol. Soc. 22*, 302-306.

Dangeard, P. A. (1896). Contribution à l'étude des Acrasiées. *Le Botaniste 5*, 1-20.

Ennis, H. L. and M. Sussman (1958a). Synergistic morphogenesis by mixtures of *Dictyostelium discoideum* wild type and aggregateless mutants. *J. Gen. Microbiol. 18*, 433-449.

Ennis, H. L. and M. Sussman (1958b). The initiator cell for slime mold aggregation. *Proc. Nat. Acad. Sci. 44*, 401-411.

Fayod, V. (1883). Beitrag zur Kenntniss niederer Myxomyceten. *Bot. Zeitung, 41*, 169-177.

Filosa, M. F. (1958). Heterocytosis in cellular slime molds. Ph.D. thesis, Princeton University.

Gamble, W. J. (1953). Orientation of the slime mold *Dictyostelium discoideum* to light. Senior thesis, Princeton University.

Gezelius, K. and B. G. Rånby (1957). Morphology and fine structure of the slime mold *Dictyostelium discoideum*. Exp. *Cell Res. 12*, 265-289.

Gregg, J. H. (1950). Oxygen utilization in relation to growth and morphogenesis of the slime mold *Dictyostelium discoideum*. *J. Exp. Zool. 114*, 173-196.

Gregg, J. H. (1956). Serological investigations of cell adhesion in the slime molds, *Dictyostelium discoideum, D. purpureum*, and *Polysphondylium violaceum*. *J. Gen. Physiol. 39*, 813-820.

Gregg, J. H. and R. D. Bronsweig (1954). The carbohydrate metabolism of the slime mold *Dictyostelium discoideum* during development. *Biol. Bull. 107*, 312.

Gregg, J. H. and R. D. Bronsweig (1956a). Dry weight loss during culmination of the slime mold *Dictyostelium discoideum. J. Cell. and Comp. Physiol. 47*, 483-488.

Gregg, J. H. and R. D. Bronsweig (1956b). Biochemical events accompanying stalk formation in the slime mold *Dictyostelium discoideum. J. Cell. and Comp. Physiol. 48*, 293-300.

Gregg, J. H., A. L. Hackney, and J. O. Krivanek (1954). Nitrogen metabolism of the slime mold *Dictyostelium discoideum* during growth and morphogenesis. *Biol. Bull. 107*, 226-235.

Gregg, J. H. and C. W. Trygstad (1958). Surface antigen defects contributing to developmental failure in aggregateless variants of the slime mold *Dictyostelium discoideum. Exper. Cell Res.* (In press.)

Grimm, M. (1895). Ueber den bau und die entwickelungsgeschichte von *Dictyostelium Mucoroides* Bref. (Résumé) *Scripta Bot. Hort. Univ. Imp. Petersburg 4*, 279-298.

Harper, R. A. (1926). Morphogenesis in *Dictyostelium. Bull. Torrey Bot. Club 53*, 229-268.

Harper, R. A. (1929). Morphogenesis in *Polysphondylium. Bull. Torrey Bot. Club 56*, 227-258.

Harper, R. A. (1932). Organization and light relations in *Polysphondylium. Bull. Torrey Bot. Club 59*, 49-84.

Hirschberg, E. (1955). Some contributions of microbiology to cancer research. *Bacteriol. Rev. 19*, 65-78.

Hirschberg, E. and G. Merson (1955). Effect of test compounds on the aggregation and culmination of the slime mold *Dictyostelium discoideum. Cancer Res. Suppl. 3*, 76-79.

Hirschberg, E. and H. P. Rusch (1950). Effects of compounds of varied biochemical action on the aggregation of the slime mold *Dictyostelium discoideum. J. Cell. Comp. Physiol. 36*, 105-113.

Hirschberg, E. and H. P. Rusch (1951). Effect of 2,4-dinitrophenol on the differentiation of the slime mold *Dictyostelium discoideum. J. Cell. Comp. Physiol. 37*, 323-336.

Jaffe, L. F. (1958) Morphogenesis in lower plants. *Ann. Rev. Plant Physiol. 9*, 359-384.

Kostellow, A. (1956). Developmental response of *Dictyostelium discoideum* to some amino acids and their analogues. Ph.D. thesis, Columbia University.

Krivanek, J. O. (1956). Alkaline phosphatase activity in the developing slime mold *Dictyostelium discoideum* Raper. *J. Exp. Zool. 133,* 459-480.

Krivanek, J. O. and R. C. Krivanek (1958) The histochemical localization of certain biochemical intermediates and enzymes in the developing slime mold, *Dictyostelium discoideum* Raper. *J. Exper. Zool. 137,* 89-115.

Labudde, B. F. (1956). A cytological study of *Dictyostelium.* Master's thesis, University of Wisconsin.

Michalska, I. and F. X. Skupienski (1939). Recherches écologique sur les Acrasièes *Polysphondylium pallidum* Olive, *Polysphondylium violaceum* Bref., *Dictyostelium mucoroides* Bref. *Comptes Rendus Acad. Sci. Paris 207,* 1239-1241.

Mühlethaler, K. (1956). Electron microscopic study of the slime mold *Dictyostelium discoideum. Amer. J. Bot. 43,* 673-678.

Nadson, G. A. (1899-1900). Des cultures du *Dictyostelium mucoroides* Bref. et des cultures pures des amibes en général. *Scripta Bot. Horti Univ. Imp. Petropolitanae 15,* 188-190. (In Russian. Résumé in French, pp. 188-190.)

Oehler, R. (1922). *Dictyostelium mucoroides* (Brefeld). *Centbl. Bakt.* (etc.) *89,* 155-156.

Olive, E. W. (1901). Preliminary enumeration of the Sorophoreae. *Proc. Amer. Acad. Arts Sci. 37,* 333-344.

Olive, E. W. (1902). Monograph of the Acrasieae. *Proc. Bost. Soc. Nat. Hist. 30,* 451-510.

Paddock, R. B. (1953). The appearance of amoebae tracks in cultures of *Dictyostelium discoideum. Science 118,* 597-598.

Palm, B. T. (1935). Ett fynd av *Dictyostelium mucoroides* i Sydsuerige (*D. Mucoroides* from South Sweden). *Svensk Bot. Tid skr. 29,* 365-366, English summary.

Pfützner-Eckert, R. (1950). Entwicklungsphysiologische untersuchungen an *Dictyostelium mucoroides* Brefeld. *Roux' Arch. Entwickl. 144,* 381-409.

Pinoy, E. (1903). Nécessité d'une symbiose microbienne pour obtenir la culture des myxomycètes. *C. R. Acad. Sci. Paris 137,* 580-581.

Pinoy, E. (1907). Rôle des bactéries dans le développment de certains myxomycètes. *Ann. Inst. Pasteur 21,* 622-656; 686-700.

Pinoy, E. (1950). Quelques observations sur la culture d'une Acrasiée. *Bull. Soc. Mycol. France 66,* 37-38.

Potts, G. (1902). Zur physiologie des *Dictyostelium mucoroides*. *Flora 91*, 281-347.

Raper, K. B. (1935). *Dictyostelium discoideum*, a new species of slime mold from decaying forest leaves. *J. Agric. Res. 50*, 135-147.

Raper, K. B. (1937). Growth and development of *Dictyostelium discoideum* with different bacterial associates. *J. Agric. Res. 55*, 289-316.

Raper, K. B. (1939). Influence of culture conditions upon the growth and development of *Dictyostelium discoideum*. *J. Agric. Res. 58*, 157-198.

Raper, K. B. (1940a). The communal nature of the fruiting process in the Acrasieae. *Amer. J. Bot. 27*, 436-448.

Raper, K. B. (1904b). Pseudoplasmodium formation and organization in *Dictyostelium discoideum*. *J. Elisha Mitchell Sci. Soc. 56*, 241-282.

Raper, K. B. (1941a). *Dictyostelium minutum*, a second new species of slime mold from decaying forest leaves. *Mycologia 33*, 633-649.

Raper, K. B. (1941b). Developmental patterns in simple slime molds. Third growth symposium. *Growth 5*, 41-76.

Raper, K. B. (1951). Isolation, cultivation, and conservation of simple slime molds. *Quart. Rev. Biol. 26*, 169-190.

Raper, K. B. (1956a). Factors affecting growth and differentiation in simple slime molds. *Mycologia 48*, 169-205.

Raper, K. B. (1956b). *Dictyostelium polycephalum* n. sp.: a new cellular slime mould with coremiform fructifications. *J. Gen. Microbiol. 14*, 716-732.

Raper, K. B. and Fennell, D. I. (1952). Stalk formation in *Dictyostelium*. *Bull. Torrey Bot. Club 79*, 25-51.

Raper, K. B. and M. S. Quinlan (1958). *Acytostelium leptosomum*: A unique cellular slime mold with an acellular stalk. *J. Gen. Microbiol. 18*, 16-32.

Raper, K. B. and N. R. Smith (1939). The growth of *Dictyostelium discoideum* upon pathogenic bacteria. *J. Bact. 38*, 431-444.

Raper, K. B. and C. Thom (1932). The distribution of *Dictyostelium* and other slime molds in soil. *J. Washington Acad. Sci. 22*, 93-96.

Raper, K. B. and C. Thom (1941). Interspecific mixtures in the Dictyosteliaceae. *Amer. J. Bot. 28*, 69-78.

Runyon, E. H. (1942). Aggregation of separate cells of *Dictyostelium* to form a multicellular body. *Collecting Net 17*, 88.

Schuckmann, W. von (1924). Zur biologie von *Dictyostelium mucoroides* Bref. *Centbl. Bakt.* (etc.) *91*, 302-309.

Schuckmann, W. von (1925). Zur morphologie und biologie von *Dictyostelium mucoroides* Bref. *Arch. Protistenk 51*, 495-529.

Shaffer, B. M. (1953). Aggregation in cellular slime moulds: *in vitro* isolation of acrasin. *Nature 171*, 975.

Shaffer, B. M. (1956a). Properties of acrasin. *Science 123*, 1172-1173.

Shaffer, B. M. (1956b). Acrasin, the chemotactic agent in cellular slime moulds. *J. Exp. Biol. 33*, 645-657.

Shaffer, B. M. (1957a). Aspects of aggregation in cellular slime moulds. I. Orientation and chemotaxis. *Amer. Nat. 91*, 19-35.

Shaffer, B. M. (1957b). Properties of slime mould amoebae of significance for aggregation. *Quart. J. Micr. Sci. 98*, 377-392.

Shaffer, B. M. (1957c). Variability of behaviour of aggregating cellular slime moulds. *Quart. J. Micr. Sci. 98*, 393-405.

Shaffer, B. M. (1958). Integration in aggregating cellular slime moulds. *Quart. J. Micr. Sci. 99*, 103-121.

Singh, B. N. (1946). Soil Acrasieae and their bacterial food supply. *Nature 157*, 133.

Singh, B. N. (1947a). Studies on soil Acrasieae: 1. Distribution of species of *Dictyostelium* in soils of Great Britain and the effect of bacteria on their development. *J. Gen. Microbiol. 1*, 11-21.

Singh, B. N. (1947b). Studies on soil Acrasieae: 2. The active life of species of *Dictyostelium* in soil and the influence thereon of soil moisture and bacterial food. *J. Gen. Microbiol. 1*, 361-367.

Skupienski, F. X. (1918). Sur la sexualité chez une espèce de Myxomycète Acrasiée *Dictyostelium mucoroides*. *C. R. Acad. Sci. Paris 167*, 960-962.

Skupienski, F. X. (1920). *Recherches sur le Cycle Évolutif des Certains Myxomycètes*. Paris. 81 pp.

Slifkin, M. K. and J. T. Bonner (1952). The effect of salts and organic solutes on the migration time of the slime mold *Dictyostelium discoideum*. *Biol. Bull. 102*, 273-277.

Slifkin, M. K. and H. S. Gutowsky (1958). Infrared spectros-
copy as a new method for assessing the nutritional requirements of the slime mold *Dictyostelium discoideum. J. Cell
Comp. Physiol. 51*, 249-257.

Sussman, M. (1951). The origin of cellular heterogeneity in the
slime molds, Dictyosteliaceae. *J. Exp. Zool. 118*, 407-417.

Sussman, M. (1952). An analysis of the aggregation stage in the
development of the slime molds, Dictyostelaceae. II. Aggregative center formation by mixtures of *Dictyostelium discoideum* wild type and aggregateless variants. *Biol. Bull.
103*, 446-457.

Sussman, M. (1954). Synergistic and antagonistic interactions
between morphogenetically deficient variants of the slime
mould *Dictyostelium discoideum. J. Gen. Microbiol. 10*,
110-120.

Sussman, M. (1955a). "Fruity" and other mutants of the cellular
slime mould. *Dictyostelium discoideum*: a study of developmental aberrations. *J. Gen. Microbiol. 13*, 295-309.

Sussman, M. (1955b). The developmental physiology of the
amoeboid slime molds. *Biochemistry and Physiology of the
Protozoa. v. 2*. 201-223. (S. Hutner and A. Lwoff, Eds.)
Academic Press, N.Y.

Sussman, M. (1956a). On the relation between growth and
morphogenesis in the slime mold *Dictyostelium discoideum.
Biol. Bull. 110*, 91-95.

Sussman, M. (1956b). The biology of the cellular slime molds.
Ann. Rev. Microbiol. 10, 21-50.

Sussman, M. and S. G. Bradley (1954). A protein growth factor
of bacterial origin required by the cellular slime molds. *Arch.
Biochem. and Biophys. 51*, 428-435.

Sussman, M. and F. Lee (1955). Interactions among variant
and wild-type strains of cellular slime molds across thin
agar membranes. *Proc. Nat. Acad. Sci. 41*, 70-78.

Sussman, M., F. Lee, and N. S. Kerr (1956). Fractionation of
acrasin, a specific chemotactic agent for slime mold aggregation. *Science 123*, 1171-1172.

Sussman, M. and E. Noël (1952). An analysis of the aggregation
stage in the development of the slime molds, Dictyosteliaceae.
I. The populational distribution of the capacity to initiate aggregation. *Biol. Bull. 103*, 259-268.

Sussman, M. and R. R. Sussman (1956). Cellular interactions during the development of the cellular slime molds. Fourteenth growth symposium. *Growth,* 125-154. Princeton University Press.

Sussman, R. R. and M. Sussman (1953). Cellular differentiation in Dictyosteliaceae: heritable modifications of the developmental pattern. *Ann. N.Y. Acad. Sci. 56,* 949-960.

Sussman, R. R., M. Sussman and F. L. Fu (1958). The chemotactic complex responsible for cellular slime mold aggregation. (Abstract from the meeting of the American Society of Bacteriologists in Chicago.)

Takeuchi, I. and M. Tazawa (1955). Studies on the morphogenesis of the slime mould, *Dictyostelium discoideum. Cytologia 20,* 157-165.

Thom, C. and K. B. Raper (1930). Myxamoebae in soil and decomposing crop residues. *J. Wash. Acad. Sci. 20,* 362-370.

van Tiegham, P. (1880). Sur quelques Myxomycètes à plasmode agrégé. *Bull. Soc. Bot. de France 27,* 317-322.

van Tieghem, P. (1884). Coenonia, genre nouveau de Myxomyctètes à plasmode agrégé. *Bull. Soc. Bot. de France 31,* 303-306.

Vuillemin, P. (1903). Une Acrasièe bactériophage. *Comp. Roud. Acad. Sci. Paris 137,* 387-389.

Whittingham, W. F. and K. B. Raper (1956). Inhibiton of normal pigment synthesis in spores of *Dictyostelium pupureum. Amer. J. Bot. 43,* 703-708.

Whittingham, W. F. and K. B. Raper (1957). Environmental factors influencing the growth and fructification of *Dictyostelium polycephalum. Amer. J. Bot. 44,* 619-627.

Wilson, C. M. (1952). Sexuality in the Acrasiales. *Proc. Nat. Acad. Sci. 38,* 659-662.

Wilson, C. M. (1953). Cytological study of the life cycle of *Dictyostelium. Amer. J. Bot. 40,* 714-718.

Wilson, C. M. and I. K. Ross (1957). Further cytological studies in the Acrasiales. *Amer. J. Bot. 44,* 345-350.

Wright, B. E. (1958). Effect of steroids on aggregation in the slime mold *Dictyostelium discoideum.* (Abstract from the meeting of the American Society of Bacteriologists in Chicago.)

Additional References Mentioned in the Text that Do Not Pertain to the Cellular Slime Molds

Adolph, E. F. (1931). *The Regulation of Size as Illustrated in Unicellular Organisms.* C. C. Thomas, Baltimore.

Bliding, C. (1938). Studien über Entwicklung und Systematik in der Gattung Enteromorpha. I. *Botaniska Notiser. Lund.*, 83-90.

Bonner, J. T. (1952). *Morphogenesis.* Princeton University Press.

Brien, P. (1937). La réorganisation de l'Eponge après dissociation par filtration et phénomènes d'involution chez *Ephydatia fluviatilis. Arch. Biol. 48*, 185-268.

Child, C. M. (1941). *Patterns and Problems of Development.* University of Chicago Press.

Cook, W. R. I. and E. J. Schwartz (1930). The life history, cytology and method of infection of *Plasmodiophora brassicae* Woron., the cause of finger-and-toe disease of cabbages and other crucifers. *Phil. Trans. Roy. Soc. London.* Series B, *281*, 283-314.

de Bary, A. (1887). *Comparative Morphology and Biology of Fungi, Mycetozoa and Bacteria.* Oxford, Clarendon Press.

Fayod, V. (1883). Beitrag Zur kenntniss niederer Myxomyceten. *Bot. Zeit. 41*, 169-177.

Galtsoff, P. S. (1929). Heteroagglutination of dissociated sponge cells. *Biol. Bull. 57*, 250-260.

Haldane, J. B. S. (1955). Some alternatives to sex. *New Biology 19*, 7-26.

Harrison, R. G. (1910). The outgrowth of the nerve fibres as a mode of protoplasmic movement. *J. Exp. Zool. 9*, 787-846.

Hartmann, M. and K. Nägler (1908). Copulation bei *Amoeba diplodea* mit selbstandigbleiben der gameten kerne während des ganze Lebenszyclus. *Stzber. Ges. Naturforsch. Freunde.*, Berlin, *1*, 112-125.

Hollande, A. and M. Enjumet (1955). Sur l'évolution et la systématique des *Labyrinthulidae. Ann. Des Sc. Nat. Zool.*, 11e serie, *17*, 357-368.

Holtfreter, J. (1943a). Properties and functions of the surface coat in amphibian embryos. *J. Exp. Zool. 93*, 251-323.

Holtfreter, J. (1943b). A study of the mechanics of gastrulation: part I. *J. Exp. Zool. 94*, 261-318.

Holtfreter, J. (1944). A study of the mechanics of gastrulation: part II. *J. Exp. Zool. 95*, 171-212.

Huxley, J. S. (1911). Some phenomena of regeneration in Sycon; with a note on the structure of its collar-cells. *Phil. Trans. Roy. Soc. London.* Series B, *202*, 165-189.

Huxley, J. S. (1921). Further studies on restitution-bodies-and free tissue-culture in Sycon. *Quar. J. Micr. Sci. 65*, 292-321.

Jennings, H. S. (1941). Inheritance in protozoa. Chap. XV in *Protozoa in Biological Research.* Eds. G. N. Calkins and F. M. Summers, Columbia University Press.

Karling, J. S. (1942). *The Plasmodiophorales.* New York.

Lederberg, J. (1954). A simple method of isolating individual microbes. *J. Bacterol. 68*, 258-259.

Ledingham, G. A. (1934). Zoöspore ciliation in the Plasmodiophorales. *Nature 133*, 534.

Moscona, A. (1957). The development in vitro of chimeric aggregates of dissociated embryonic chick and mouse cells. *Proc. Nat. Acad. Sci. 43*, 184-194.

Nägler, K. (1909). Entwicklungsgeschicht-liche studienuber Amöben. *Arch. Protistenk. 15*, 1-53.

Ray, D. L. and R. E. Hayes (1954). *Hartmannella astronyxis*: a new species of free-living ameba. *J. Morphol. 95*, 159-188.

Renn, C. E. (1935). A mycetozoan parasite of *Zostera marina. Nature 135*, 544.

Rothschild, Lord (1956). *Fertilization,* Methuen, London.

Smith, G. M. (1955). *Crytogramic Botony* v.I. 2nd ed. Mc-Graw-Hill, New York.

Thaxter, R. (1892). On the Myxobacteriaceae, a new order of Schizomycetes. *Bot. Gaz. 17*, 389-406.

Thompson, D'A. W. (1942). *Growth and Form,* 2nd ed. Macmillan, New York.

Townes, P. L. and J. Holtfreter (1955). Directed movements and selective adhesion of embryonic amphibian cells. *J. Exp. Zool. 128*, 53-120.

Trinkaus, P. J. (1957). Personal communication.

Twitty, V. C. (1949). Developmental analysis of amphibian pigmentation. *Ninth Growth Symposium*, 133-161.

Tyler, A. (1942). Developmental processes and energetics. *Quart. Rev. Biol. 17*, 197-212, 339-353.

Watson, S. W. (1955). Personal communication.

Weiss, P. (1929). Erzwingung elementarer Strukturver schied-enheiten am in vitro wachsenden gewebe. Die Wirkung mechanischer Spannung auf Richtung und Intensität des Gewebewachtums und ihre Analyse. *Roux' Arch. Entwickl. 116*, 438-554.

Weiss, P. (1934). In vitro experiments on the factors determining the course of the outgrowing nerve fibre. *J. Exp. Zool. 68*, 393-448.

Weiss, P. (1945). Experiments on cell and axon orientation in vitro: the role of colloidal exudates in tissue organization. *J. Exp. Zool. 100*, 353-386.

Weiss, P. and G. Andres (1952). Experiments on the fate of embryonic cells (chick) disseminated by the vascular route. *J. Exp. Zool. 121*, 449-488.

Wenrich, D. H. (1954). Sex in protozoa: a comparative review. *Sex in Microorganisms*, A.A.A.S., Washington, D.C.

Wilson, H. V. (1907). On some phenomena of coalescence and regeneration in sponges. *J. Exp. Zool. 5*, 245-258.

Wilson, M. and E. J. Cadman (1928). The life-history and cytology of *Reticularia lycoperdon*. *Bull. Trans. Roy. Soc.*, Edinburgh, *55*, 555-608.

Index

The Library of Congress has catalogued this book as follows:

BONNER, JOHN TYLER. The cellular slime molds. Princeton, Princeton University Press, 1959, 150 p. illus. 23 cm. (Investigations in the biological sciences, no. 1) 1. Myxomycetes. I. Title. (Series) QH.1.I 46 no. 1 589.29 59-5590 Library of Congress

The Library of Congress has catalogued the series in which this book appears as follows:

INVESTIGATIONS in the biological sciences. no. 1—Princeton, Princeton University Press, 1959- no. 22 cm. 1. Biology—Collected works. QH.1.I 46 574.082 59-7034 Library of Congress